D1478388

# BY THE WIND

*Cornet*

*Little Dipper* designed by Starling Burgess

# BY THE WIND

*by*

RICHARD BAUM

VAN NOSTRAND REINHOLD COMPANY

NEW YORK   CINCINNATI   TORONTO   LONDON   MELBOURNE

Van Nostrand Reinhold Company Regional Offices:
New York    Cincinnati    Chicago    Millbrae    Dallas

Von Nostrand Reinhold Company International Offices:
London              Toronto              Melbourne

COPYRIGHT © 1962, 1973 BY
LITTON EDUCATIONAL PUBLISHING, INC.

Library of Congress Catalog Card Number
ISBN 0-442-20608-9

Published by VAN NOSTRAND REINHOLD COMPANY
450 West 33rd Street, New York, N.Y. 10001

Published simultaneously in Canada by
VAN NOSTRAND REINHOLD LIMITED

3   5   7   9   11   13   15   16   14   12   10   8   6   4   2

To All Those Who Adventure on Great Waters
In Small Ships

## *Preface*

The cruises here recounted were made in *Little Dipper,* a thirty-five foot cutter designed by Starling Burgess. Her building began in 1932 with the best of materials going into her, but owing to the Depression her builder, Joel Johnson of Bridgeport, Connecticut, was eventually instructed to finish her off as economically as possible. Her lack of finish was apparent when I bought her in 1946, and sticklers for "yachtiness" would find it apparent still. It suited me, however, because it enabled me to buy a longer and abler boat than I could otherwise have afforded, and one designed by as fine a designer as ever lived.

I call *Little Dipper* a cutter because her hull is in the cutter tradition, deep and relatively narrow. In a fresh breeze this kind of hull may not stand up to its canvas as well as beamier ones, but to my mind that disadvantage is offset by a cutter's speed in light airs, easy motion in a seaway, and, when the wind begins to squeal and seas pile up to spreader height, greater ultimate stability.

I bought my ship to cruise in, as widely as I could. There is no nobler sport than cruising and none more rewarding. I'm not sure, in fact, that "sport" entirely covers cruising. In an age when man seems bent on dominating nature at risk of losing contact with the realities that gave him birth, it may be that exposure to wind and weather, the sight of wide horizons, the solitude of quiet anchorages, and an occasional consciousness that life depends on skill and prudence in a fog or gale are sheer necessities. At any rate, these and the joy of them are what I've tried to celebrate in the following pages.

My thanks are due the editors of *The Rudder* and *Yachting* for making available material published in those magazines in somewhat different form.

                                          RICHARD BAUM

*Stonington, Conn.*

# Contents

# List of Illustrations

# BY THE WIND

# CHAPTER I

## *Across the Gulf of Maine*

Cool air off the Atlantic flowed over the headlands of Cape Ann and brought the smell of ocean distances into Rockport harbor. In the center of the harbor *Little Dipper* had seemed bolted to the reflection of her hull. Now she lifted a length of rode clear of rippled water and swung back upon her anchor.

Minutes later the mainsail had gone up the mast and Andy had heaved the anchor onto the foredeck. As the boat began sliding toward the harbor entrance, the jib fluttered up the headstay in time to the swing of Andy's shoulders. He had not sailed with me before, but the way he worked promised an able partner for the passage.

I knew the Doc a little better. Short, bluff jawed, hands tucked between his belt and a rounded waistline, he stood beside the shrouds to hail a friend aboard a cabin cruiser. "We're bound for Nova Scotia," he called. "Straight across—without an engine!"

The man looked around, but the Doc turned aft toward where his wife watched us from a dinghy at our anchorage. He boomed across the widening distance, "I'm off to battle the elements! Your husband and the father of your child! And don't forget to put the cat out!"

As I gave the wheel a spoke to clear the breakwater I saw Andy's red head turn toward the Doc. Andy looked puzzled, but not disturbed.

Beyond the breakwater the tops of Cape Ann's outlying ledges shone white in a sparkling sea. Farther out, where all day sea and sky had met at a clear horizon, the easterly air had

1

raised a wall of dark brown fog. I streamed the log and put the boat on a compass course to leave the ledges well to starboard. "That fog'll be in," I guessed, "before we're in the clear."

The Doc gazed at the fog.

Andy looked overside at the water rustling past the hull. "She really slips along," he said, "in this light air!"

Doc                                          Andy

High outriders of the fog streamed toward us through the sky and soon obscured the sun and chilled the air. Thickening above the masthead, the fog floated in puffs past sails and shrouds, darkened the deck with moisture. Rapidly the fog veiled all but a few yards of water beyond the bowsprit. Glancing aft, I saw only the revolving log line and a trail of bubbles vanishing under thick gray air. Fog had enclosed us. We were at sea.

When the log showed we had dropped the ledges astern we hardened sheets and came on the wind. The boat took some heel and, with a watery lisping at the bow, occasionally a splash, sailed smoothly through the murk toward Yarmouth, Nova Scotia, two hundred miles to the eastward.

"This breeze won't quite let us lay the course," I told the Doc when he offered to take the wheel. "Work her to windward when you can, but watch the compass too. We'll want to plot the course you make."

Moments later, our heads bent over a chart spread on the cockpit floor, Andy and I felt the ship lose heel. A glance aloft showed the sails softening in the foggy air.

"Guess I'm pinching her," the Doc said, "but if I look at the compass how can I watch the sails? Maybe if I was wall-eyed or something—"

"Just check the compass now and then," I told him. "Average it out."

Looking upward as he eased her off the breeze, the Doc observed, "Right now is when I think we should turn on the engine—if we had an engine. Then we could steer a straight course and tomorrow we'd know where we were. Which I think is important."

"You're aboard of a windjammer," Andy said, well pleased.

The Doc sighed. "The whole thing beats me. I mean as a form of entertainment. But my mind's still open."

Through the waning afternoon we moved alone upon the fog-veiled ocean. We heard no other vessels and no horns. All sails drawing, heeled by a southeasterly breeze, *Little Dipper* slipped steadily through the water and gently rose and fell on long swells coming out of the fog abeam. Now and then her masthead nodded, her bow dipped and rose again. The breeze only ruffled the surface of the deepening water beneath her keel, but the log showed she was making a good four knots. When evening's chill and darkness closed in around the cockpit, a drink of whiskey went down smooth and warm.

"This seafaring makes whiskey taste good," the Doc said, "but every time I see those bunks below I think about my nice four-poster back in Rockport." Shivering a little inside his oilskins, he turned the collar of his shirt up around the plumpness of his neck. "That bed," he went on, "makes an interesting subject for discussion. Jean's family had that bed for generations. They built it in Vermont and then they took it out to California—in a covered wagon, they claim. When they got tired of California they brought it back to New England. I got it when I married her. I got Jean and her mother and the four-poster."

"Quite a haul, Doc," Andy said.

"Well," the Doc said, "it all averages out—like steering this boat." He said with feeling, "It's a wonderful four-poster!"

Soon after supper Andy went below. Since the Doc had drawn the first watch I might have turned in too, but the wet blackness through which my little ship was sailing, the knowledge that she was out upon the ocean and getting farther out, made me linger in the cockpit. The barometer was steady. The breeze continued light.

A dark bulk behind the wheel, the Doc spoke above the rustle of water around the hull. "I'm wondering," he said, "why people do this kind of thing. It's not bad now except for this fog. But anything might happen. Anything. And who would know?"

"Doc," I said, "I guess that's part of it."

Dawn came during my second watch, and perhaps because I had dozed the light breaking up the blackness came unexpectedly. Surprisingly, it seemed, we would not sail all the way in darkness, but would have daylight too. First the cabin house with the dinghy lashed upon it, then the curve of the deck and its dripping lifelines, finally sails and rigging all the way to the masthead, stood out clearly in the gray light. Discovering I was cold and stiff, I flapped my arms for warmth. When I went below to shake Andy awake, hunger made me smell the coffee and taste the bacon I planned to cook.

On deck a moment later, the light had brightened all around the moving ship, revealing a low overcast of clouds and under them, across wide distances of steely water, scattered banks and layers of fog. Some of these layers were rumpled and folded back upon themselves like blankets, like the bedding of a company of giants who had slept upon the sea.

"What's the course?" Andy asked, coming on deck in oilskins.

"By the wind."

Plotted on the chart, the notes each helmsman had made during the night of his course and mileage gave a crooked line from Rockport that placed us seventy miles east northeast of Cape Ann. But we had sailed by the wind all night, averaging out our compass readings, sometimes on the course to Yarmouth but oftener forced north. The crooked line was only an estimate and by the look of the morning there would be no horizon and no sun, no chance to use a sextant. In those foggy waters there might be none for a week.

"The direction finder may pay its way," I said to Andy, "when we come to close the coast."

All day the southeasterly breeze gave the cutter a steady heel and kept her moving. All day a little wave curled off her bow, and her round flank went sliding smoothly through tranquil water. Once we heard a steamer's foghorn far off, muffled in a distant fogbank. Otherwise, so far as eye and ear could tell, we sailed an ocean as vacant as in John Cabot's time.

In the afternoon we ran through miles of kelp and later a shark's black fin appeared astern. For half an hour the fin wagged lazily along behind the rotator of the log, but made no pass at it. Finally the fin submerged, leaving the fog-strewn ocean as vacant as before.

At evening a fogbank astern cleared enough to show us a huge red sun touching the sea and kindling it to crimson, then seeming to melt and vanish in a pool of fire. That pool brought to mind other pools that would blaze behind it to the westward, horizon after horizon, measuring out the water we had put between ourselves and land.

Face reddened by the cold red light, the Doc admitted the splendor of the sunset. "Still," he added, "I keep wondering why people want to stick their necks out to the Atlantic Ocean."

"Well," Andy said, looking out across it, "it's a pretty good ocean."

"Maybe you didn't see that shark."

The bow lifted to a sea and the sea's back came swelling aft along the rail. The ship lifted a saucy transom to the afterglow behind her and cut cleanly through the water toward the darkness rising in the east.

We held the starboard tack all night, sometimes under a cloudy scattering of stars. The breeze freshened and the ship heeled more and began a rhythmic pitching, each downward movement of the bow throwing a splashing phosphorescence out across the blackness of the sea. Toward midnight the glittering bow wave began to show strange plunging lights. From behind the wheel I heard the splashing grow erratic and unduly loud. Suddenly beneath the surface off to port something big, streaming with phosphorescence, sped toward the middle of the hull as if to strike it broadside on and crack it open. Only after thinking of torpedos did I remember porpoises. Porpoises followed us all night, playing in the bow wave, shaming our steady progress. Maybe, on summer nights a thousand years before, their ancestors had played around Viking longboats furrowing these same waters.

The second dawn brought a further freshening of the southeast breeze, increasing cold, and rain. Hard on the wind, unable quite to lay the course, the ship heeled more and her big masthead jib began an angry luffing. Braced against the leaning cockpit, I took a turn of the sheet around a winch and cranked it in. The taut sheet came in hard.

In the brightening light the seas grew bigger, eddying and hissing as they flowed aft along the hull. A flurry of rain peppered the sails, drummed on the deck and dinghy, and shut down visibility. The flurry passed, but outward from the ship in all directions heavy clouds hung from the overcast, promising more rain and barring hope of sun. In the freshening breeze the steel gray surface of the sea was torn with whitecaps.

Leaning to the heel of the cockpit and watching the tall rig's slant against the windy sky, I thought of loads building up on shrouds and spreaders and imagined the clench and grip of lofty splices. It was good to remember the careful check I'd made of the pins and turnbuckles that held that rig up there on the swaying mast and held the mast in the boat.

A sea thumped hard against *Little Dipper*'s underbody. A dollop of water flew across the foredeck and streamed aft along the deck to gurgle outboard through the scupper. The boom tugged at its four part sheet, tautening the manila and squeezing out blown drops of water. Settling deeper in the seas, the ship began throwing out a bow wave.

"Can't give her much for her cabin layout," Andy said when he climbed on deck to take his watch. "But she's got a kindly motion." After a look at the day he too glanced aloft. "She'll be kindly on her rig."

When I went below to cook breakfast the cabin was resounding to the steady rush of water past the planking, and I could feel the ship's weight rising to the seas, then settling, moving fast. Breakfast was cooked and most of the dishes washed when the Doc rolled out of his blankets. Standing in his underwear, clutching a deck beam to brace himself against the cabin's motion, he peered out the scuttle. Above in the cockpit, Andy stood before the wheel in streaming oilskins, his legs braced wide apart, his eyes narrowed against a lash of rain. The Doc shuddered visibly, and sat down to pull on dungarees.

"This is Sunday," he muttered. "Usually on Sundays I stay in the four-poster until ten o'clock. I remember once I stayed till noon. And Jean cooked a cheese souffle." He sighed. "Not that anything like that matters now."

He ate heartily and went on deck.

A plot of the night's courses placed the ship halfway between Mount Desert Rock off the coast of Maine and Lurcher Lightship fifteen miles off Yarmouth. During the morning I tried to bring the lightship in on the direction finder, and toward noon, with the aerial looking dead to windward, the lightship's signal sounded in the headphones. Moments later Seal Island at the southern tip of Nova Scotia came in from the same direction. Crossed with the line of our dead reckoning, the radio bearing placed us thirty miles to the northwest of the lightship.

With fog a constant possibility we planned to sight the lightship and so fix our position before closing the coast. We also wanted to use a Bay of Fundy tide which the current tables promised would be running southward along the coast that afternoon. We held on eastward for several hours, then put down the helm. With a noisy flogging of headsails *Little Dipper* came up into the wind, lay over on the port tack, and gained new way. Soon she was full and by on her southward heading, rising to the larger seas and smacking little ones aside.

The wind kept strengthening and the little ship stepped out. Carrying main, staysail, and masthead jib, she dipped her rail in the broken water. Sometimes the crest of a wave flew across her bow and spray was thrown against the dinghy. Rain squalls hung from the overcast, shutting down visibility when they passed over us, then letting us see for miles through a layer of clear air between the overcast and the gray sea. Between tricks at the wheel the Doc and Andy slept below. Hoping to close the coast before darkness came, I studied coastal charts and checked the lightship's bearing on the direction finder. As the afternoon passed the signal strengthened, but no lightship appeared on the spread of ocean off the bow.

"I've been doing some thinking," the Doc said once when all of us were in the cockpit. "That direction finder just gives you a line from you to the lightship. It doesn't say whether you're going or coming on that line."

"The signal's getting louder," I said.

"So's the signal from Seal Island."

"Seal Island's beyond the lightship. We're moving toward it, too."

"Here's what I've been thinking," the Doc said. "Maybe our dead reckoning didn't average out. Maybe it's all cockeyed and we're moving up on both those points, from the *south*—to hit Seal Island first."

Grabbing the cockpit coaming as the ship lunged, he stabbed a finger at the chart to indicate Seal Island's surrounding rocks and ledges. "We may need wheels. Probably about dark!"

"Look, Doc," Andy said, "you better get some sleep."

"I just want to know if this possibility's been considered."

"The compass says we're going south, not north."

Momentarily a light appeared to dawn for the Doc, but he rubbed his wet beard dubiously. "I certainly hope you characters know what you're doing with that direction finder. Because I'm doing it with you."

Andy grinned. "Looks like hope's your only hope."

Disappearing down the companionway toward the warmth and blankets in the cabin, the Doc fired a last shot over his shoulder. "Not my only hope. Us plump fellas float pretty good."

Somewhat later his face appeared in the scuttle. "This is a medical report. I have just had my first bowel movement since we put to sea."

"That been worrying you?" I asked.

"Some. Only now I guess I was just averaging out. Because after I said I'd come on this death defying voyage I had half a dozen movements in an hour."

We waved him down.

Toward four o'clock the lightship's signal was broad off the bow. With another flog of headsails, and a plunge of the bow and rattle of dishes below, we tacked ship again and headed east. An hour later the lightship still had not appeared and another tack seemed called for. But as the Doc and Andy braced themselves to handle lines in the pitching cockpit my eye was caught by a dim blue spot miles away across the whitecapped sea.

"Bring her over," the Doc said. "We're all set."

Far out ahead, hidden as the foredock rose to a sea, revealed as the deck came down, the blue spot hung motionless on the horizon.

"Land ahead!" I sang out. "Fine on the windward bow."

On the high side of the cockpit Andy's wet sou'wester turned ahead.

"I got it," Andy said. "That's land."

A hard gust struck the sails, and the plunging ship took more heel, her lee deck scooping water. A sea lurched up ahead and tried to knock her bow downwind. Her bow knocked the sea straight up and it splashed across the foredeck. Her keel brought her up and she went driving on, spray flying.

I leaned overside to pat her underbody. "Sail," I murmured, "Little lady, sail!"

Lee rail half the time awash, she showed what she could do. We left the lightship somewhere to the south, and, hoping the last of the ebbing tide would carry us upwind toward Yarmouth, we drove east for the distant headland. It was a race against the turn of the tide and the approach of darkness. North of the area we thought we'd fetch, lay unlighted rocks and shoals, and a few miles south of Yarmouth the coast bristled with islets, tide rips, reefs, and offered few lights or whistles. One of that coast's tides would carry a ship fifteen miles. It was not a coast to drive a ship toward after dark unless you knew exactly where you were.

The wind strengthened and the seas grew steeper. Still unidentified, the headland moved across our bow to port, telling us the tide was working for us, setting us south. Slowly the headland rose above the horizon and grew larger. The ship was heeled far over, her lee rail now continuously awash. A white bow wave was shooting out from her leeward shoulder and roaring above the gusty wind. As she went swinging, plunging through the seas, some of the bigger ones slapped their backs against the lower coaming.

"If we had an engine," the Doc said above the noise of wind and ship, "we could home on the lightship and steer straight for Yarmouth, dark or not. We'd know we had it made."

Down on the lee side of the cockpit Andy put his shoulder to a winch and managed to crank in an inch of jib sheet. He climbed back to the windward side, was thrown against the Doc by a lunge of the ship, and clapped the Doc's hunched shoulders. "Doc," he shouted, "you're windjamming! Now you're living!"

The Doc looked up at the threatening sky. "But for how long?"

Somewhere behind us, out beyond a low roof of clouds, the sun had begun to set. Although growing larger, the headland was increasingly obscure. Sometimes rain squalls blotted it out completely. The cold afternoon was darkening. Night was on the way. Wind and sea were rising, the leaning mast and rigging absorbing greater strains.

"The wheel's all yours, Doc," I said, making room for him to slide behind it. "Andy, we better take in the jib while we can."

We crawled forward none too soon. When Andy slacked the halyard the big sail whipped frenziedly, threatening to flog itself to pieces. Riding the bowsprit and tugging the sail down the stay, I was plunged deep in water fresh from Labrador.

"A light!" the Doc sang out from the wheel. "Off to windward!"

Helping me lash the jib to the bowsprit, Andy spotted the light and grunted, "Two flashes." Back in the cockpit, the chart showed a two flash light on Cape St. Mary, Nova Scotia, some fifteen miles to the north of Yarmouth. That made our headland Brier Island at the entrance to the Bay of Fundy. We were headed between that island and the cape, toward St. Mary's Bay.

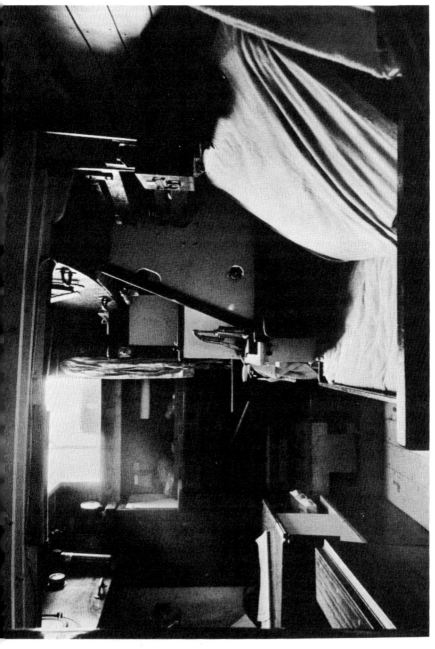

*Cornet*

Looking aft in *Little Dipper's* cabin

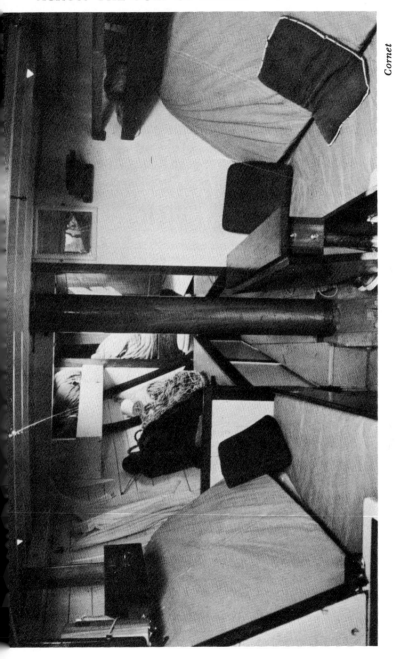

*Cornet*

Looking forward in *Little Dipper's* cabin

Relieved of her jib, the ship was eased and stood up better to her remaining canvas. The rising seas made harder going, but as darkness thickened she showed her power and steadily lunged on. The flashes of the light came closer, brightening and growing longer.

Below in the swaying cabin I pulled on dry clothes and wondered what our strategy should be. Yarmouth lay almost dead to windward and the tide soon would turn to run north—and run hard. Climbing into a cockpit boisterous with wind and the noise of the seas, I put the problem to the crew.

"Any harbor," the Doc asked, "in this bay ahead?"

"No. But maybe the cape'll give us a lee and a place to anchor."

We held on, beginning to bring the light abeam, but uncertain in the darkening night how far off the light might be. Since the entrance to the bay was ten miles wide, we gave the light a generous mile or more. As its flashes came abeam to starboard we saw more lights up the bay, lighted windows in houses, the headlights of a car moving along the shore, but in the darkness the shoreline itself was invisible. The bottom sloped so gradually that a cast of the lead told little. Wanting to stay well off unlighted docks or fishtraps, we got little lee from the fresh wind, but inside the cape the seas were lower, the going smoother. Still deeply heeled, the ship gained speed and went crashing through the night like a heavy projectile.

"Let's slack off the main and put her on her feet," I said to Andy, who had the wheel. "Jog her along a mile or so under the staysail, then bring her about and jog her back by compass. I'll cook a good hot meal."

The Doc payed out the mainsheet, the ship stood up and slowed. I went below. With lanterns lighted and the stove throwing out warmth, the cabin made a snug and peaceful contrast to the hurlyburly of the afternoon.

Ham and beans were beginning to sizzle and smell good on

the stove, tea water was steaming, when the Doc's voice sounded
in the cockpit. "Where's that light on the cape? It's disappeared."

In a moment Andy's voice said, "Fog."

I put my head out the hatch. The wind singing through
the darkness was moist against my face, and colder. A huge halo
of lighted fog had formed around the running light in the
shrouds. Ashore only two or three lights were visible. They too
wore halos and were dimming. Within a minute all lights
ashore had vanished and fog had enclosed the boat in solid
blackness. Faintly, an unknown distance across the wind, a foghorn on the cape sounded doleful warning.

Devoured in the windy cockpit as we jogged back along our
compass course, ham and beans were hot and juicy, tea and
sugar bracing. But even with full bellies the prospect of hardening sheets again and sailing out past the foghorn into a wind
that had diminished little, the thought of a nightlong thrash to
windward along a tide-scoured coast in fog, was not inviting.
Going forward to check the foredeck, I stumbled and fell. I was
tired.

"We could use the lead," I said to Andy, "and work her inshore out of the bobble, and anchor. Then tomorrow we could
ride the ebb down the coast."

Shoulders hunched against the wind, the Doc looked hopeful.

"You're the skipper," Andy said.

"You mean you'd play it different?"

Above the wheel his wet face gleamed in light from the cabin.
"Wouldn't anchor a ship of mine against an unknown shore in
fog—shore that might be a lee shore by morning. You'd probably get away with it, but I wouldn't call it judgement."

Neither, I thought, would I.

"We'll sail her out of here," I said. "Doc, you've got the first
watch. Keep her sou'west by the compass until the foghorn's
abeam. Then we'll read the log and put her on the wind. We

won't start tacking until we figure we're ten miles offshore."

"Another night," the Doc said.

"I'll take your watch," Andy offered. "This little hooker's all boat. She's fun to sail!"

Andy sailed her well offshore while the Doc and I slept below. And except for two hours when the Doc relieved him Andy sailed her all that night. "Thought you'd been overworking," he told me in the morning. "Maybe someone else should do the cooking."

That's the kind of man to cruise with.

By morning the sails hung lifeless and we lay becalmed on a circle of glassy water walled in by dense white fog. Sunshine filtered through the fog and warmed us, bringing summer back, but all that day and most of the next both fog and calm hung on. Occasionally a light air filled the jib, starting the vessel ghosting, but the airs soon died. Most of the time there was no air at all. We heard no ships in the fog, no horns or whistles, and only the changing bearings of the lightship on the direction finder told us that we were being washed up and down the coast by the Bay of Fundy's tides. Dozing, sunbathing, we floated in a limbo that might have been anywhere on the planet—or off it.

"If you crazy guys weren't engine haters," the Doc pointed out, "we could home on the lightship, get a fix, and motor straight to Yarmouth."

"We could have taken the steamer to Yarmouth," Andy said, "if getting there was all we cared about."

The Doc stared at him. "You mean you don't care when we get there?" He threw his arms wide at the fog. "You like it here?"

Flat on the deck, sunning himself, Andy grinned. "Sure I like it here. No roll, sunshine, all the time in the world. This is cruising."

Seated on the dinghy on the cabin house, the Doc crossed his legs and pulled his feet in under him. Resembling a Buddha in dungarees, he lifted a didactic finger. "Aboard this boat we've got two violently conflicting philosophies—you characters', and mine. We're at different poles." He went on, "I've been doing some thinking and I've figured out why I'm here. As I see it, my wife's responsible."

"How do you figure that?"

"It all goes back to the start of our marriage. I married her when I got back from doctoring the infantry on Guadalcanal. You know how things were then. Everyone who got within a thousand miles of that lousy island was a hero. I mean to their wives. Which is all right at the time, but women never forget that kind of thing. So when I got this invitation Guadalcanal came up again, and somehow she persuaded me that deep down beneath the civilized veneer I was naturally a battler of the elements. The Viking type. Her hero. The horrible thing is, I kind of fell for it myself. And when I get home I'm going to beat her. If I get home."

"Honest John," I said, "stop battling the elements and have a beer."

"First I want to make one point. Mankind has taken centuries to conquer the elements and get safe. And now guys like you want to go out and conquer them all over again. I hate to say it, because it's two against one and I'm the one, but to a man with a philosophy like mine you windjamming people are barbarians. Where's that beer?"

Toward evening a southerly breeze rippled the little circle of water visible within the fog. Lee-bowing an ebbing tide, we began to slide inshore toward Yarmouth and its protecting arm, Cape Fourchu. Nearing land as the air grew cold and the fog darkened, we heard the Fourchu diaphone ahead and to the north. For an hour we held on, thinking we might slip around the cape with the last of the southward-going tide, the last of the breeze. But the breeze was failing and the diaphone's bellow began to move across our bow to starboard, closing the harbor mouth, telling us the tide had turned.

We put an anchor over as a safeguard against drifting too close inshore, and felt the anchor scrape bottom at twenty fathoms. We payed out more line. The anchor bit and held, and the ship swung to an accelerating current. By nightfall the rode was shivering with strain. On deck the sound of a bow wave, in the cabin the wash of water around the hull, gave a sense that we were being towed.

"I've enjoyed swapping philosophies and lies with you characters," the Doc said as we passed glasses and the whiskey bottle around the cabin table before supper. "These last two days actually haven't been so bad. If I could be sure the anchor would hold, I'd say we were having fun."

"You're beginning to get the tempo," I said.

"The trouble is I can't be sure."

Fog made the night black as coal. There was no breeze, but when I came on deck to relieve the anchor watch, three layers of wool clothing with oilskins over them did not prevent the cold from seeping through. The Doc disappeared down the companionway, and I felt my way forward along the deck. A flashlight lighted up the rode and the fog around it, but could not penetrate the fog to where the rode met water. The tide had slackened. The bow wave was only a ripple, floating aft in bubbles. When I turned back, the lantern in the cockpit was only a faint glimmer, just visible. It brightened as I neared it. Thick flakes of fog were drifting through its light like falling snow.

I sat in the cockpit and heard the tide go slack, the last rustle at the bow fade into silence. The only sound was the drip of fog-soaked sails. There was no roll, though now and then the ocean heaved and the ship slowly rose and settled. That same swell would be fingering into spruce walled coves in Maine, coves where *Little Dipper* had laid at anchor in other years, and would again. Maybe that swell was coming in from some disturbance which days before had thrown surf far up warm beaches in the tropics, beaches my little ship might some day see.

Fog drifted white and thick across the lantern's aura. The ocean slumbered, faintly stirring. Off in the blackness shoreward the diaphone on Fourchu bawled, raising echoes in wild hills inland. The diaphone bawled again and echoed, far off, lonely-sounding, fading into the murmur of the ocean night. Lazily, a halyard slapped against the mast. Sounds you do not hear ashore . . .

At dawn the fog lifted. After breakfast we drank a second pot of coffee in the cockpit in brilliant sunshine. All around us, apparently miles away in all directions across sun-spangled water, the horizon looked clean and clear. The ship seemed anchored in mid-ocean. But the diaphone was still sounding, loud enough to be close at hand. As we hunted for it a breeze sprang up and rolled away a remnant of the fog that had clung, invisible, against the shore. Out of that fog, a mile or two away, came Cape Fourchu, a low headland with a lighthouse on it. Back of the Cape a line of blue hills appeared and on them woods, pastures, and white houses—farms of a foreign land.

We lingered in the cockpit, delaying the labor of getting up the anchor, delaying the moment when the trip would end. At length we hoisted sail, brought the anchor up on the windlass, and tacked around the Cape. From there the breeze was fair, and we stood inshore with the boom broad off for the mouth of a tidal river. Once in the river we ran between green shores while ranks of wavelets sparkled alongside and whispered secrets to the hull.

The Doc looked astern at the ocean lying in the sun. "We made it," he said. "We conquered the elements, and I admit there's a certain satisfaction. Maybe I won't beat my wife. Maybe I'm even glad I came!"

At the mast, tidying a halyard coil for the moment when we would lower sail, Andy smiled at me. I thought I read his mean-

ing. We hadn't had the fair wind and summer weather we had
hoped for. But we had seen our landfall rise above a roughening sea. We had been alive in brain and muscle, and alive to the
light and space and weather of our world.

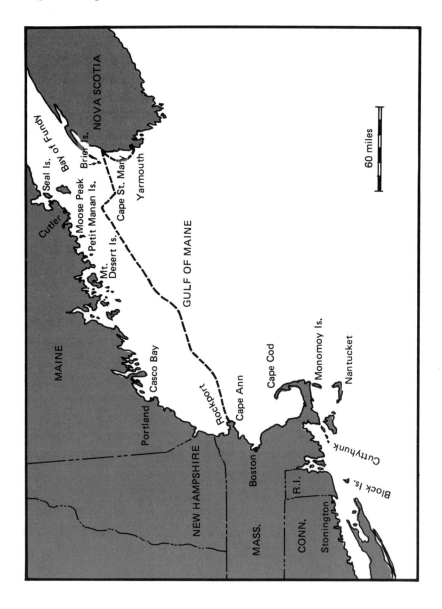

# CHAPTER II

## By Sail to the Caribbean

My thirty-five foot cutter suits me well for cruising the New England coast. She is weatherly and rugged, and along the coast no vessel of her size keeps up with her. In September of '55, however, three of us were minded to sail her on the open ocean to the Caribbean.

You can, of course, go south along the coast, but that lands you in Florida with the best of the Caribbean a thousand miles to the eastward against a booming Trade—a hard thrash even with an engine, and *Little Dipper* has no engine. On the other hand, the westerlies of the North Atlantic offer a sailing ship free easting to Bermuda. From there to St. Thomas in the Virgin Islands the course is south, which means that when you reach the Trade it will blow abeam instead of in your teeth. And then, come spring, that same Trade guarantees a glorious run and reach along the Antilles and up through the Bahamas to the southwesterlies of the eastern coast. With luck, a free wind all the way.

The saltiest heads I knew approved this strategy, and as summer ended McVitty and I began readying the ship for sea. Andy, our navigator, wrote that he had broken out his sextant and shot the sun from Biddeford beach.

It was cold that fall. October's winds blew hard. At the shipyard there were days when leaves and shavings whirled wildly among the sheds, days when our ship's tall mast leaned over and her dock lines creaked. Sometimes the tin roof of the shed in which we painted water cans and other gear thundered so loudly in the gusts that we stopped our brushes to wait for the

21

noise to end. At such times I thought of the wind combing the ocean a hundred miles off Montauk and of how big the seas would be. And of my own inexperience on deep water.

The professional captain of a big motorsailer warned us about the Trade. "Even in our boat," he said, "there've been days when we turned and ran."

When we told him we planned to put the Trade abeam by going out to Bermuda, his jaw clamped shut and his eyes snapped ferociously.

"You'd be foolish to go out there in November," an experienced yachtsman told us. "November's worse than January."

Other voices, at least as seasoned, prophesied no doom.

"If you heave her to," a former skipper of the Offshore Patrol advised, "try taking the pull of the trysail on the windward sheet. That puts a bag in the sail and stops her."

"She's built for it," said the boss of the Mystic Shipyard.

November was a week gone when we brought her around to Stonington under a new dacron mainsail, cut smaller than her regular main and free of roach and battens. Another week went by before food and gear were stowed. Finally an evening call to LaGuardia Field indicated that no late hurricanes were whirling up the coast. The next afternoon, with the sound of McVitty's final carpentry floating up from the cabin, mooring lines splashed overside and *Little Dipper* slipped down the harbor on a light southeasterly. A low sun glowed behind an autumn haze, but our fingers felt the cold. Beyond Fisher's Island, bare with fall, Block Island Sound looked gray and wintry.

At dark, closehauled to enter the Gulf Stream some sixty miles west of where we hoped to leave it, we took our departure from a gong under the bluffs of Montauk. For an hour or two the lights of draggers glimmered across the blackness of the water, then disappeared below the horizon. Between us and the Caribbean lay fifteen hundred miles of November ocean.

That night a strengthening southerly got the off watch out of bed to reef the main, and shoved us off our course. As a gray dawn lighted up a gray ocean we were hard on the wind, slogging into whitecapped seas with spray flying across the bow, and sheets and windward shrouds bar taut. Wearing oilskins over wool clothing, we clung to the cockpit's weather side, and shivered—and the six hundred miles to Bermuda began to look like long ones. But as we drove harder through a rising sea the wind continued veering. By noon we were over on the starboard tack and laying the course again. An hour later a line squall cleared the sky, and the sun came out. Soon we were reaching southward in a fresh nor'wester. The ship's motion eased. Behind the helmsman the log began to hum. Our strategy was working.

When I came on deck that night, Andy said from behind the wheel, "We're in the Stream."

I put a hand overside. The water rushing past was warm.

Morning came off clear and bright. We found ourselves in a different world. The sun was hot, the light dazzling. Long ocean seas were swelling up astern, their depths translucent blue, their tumbling crests pure white. Gulf weed floated past, golden in the sunlight. Here in mid-November, in the Stream of whose squalls and fierceness we had heard so much, it was a beautiful summer day, without a sign of squall, without a cloud in the hot blue sky.

We got down to underclothes to enjoy the sun, and after two nights at sea the warmth soon made us sleepy. By afternoon even the helmsman dozed, for the breeze had died and the bright ocean was only gently heaving. All night we lay becalmed under stars.

The next day November asserted itself, and by noon we were back in wool and oilskins with half a gale blowing out of the west. Mindful of the Gulf Stream's reputation, I thought it wise to reef and finally take in the main. We soon were glad we had, for under staysail alone the ship moved fast in a roughening sea, her lee rail frequently awash. Wind and sea kept rising, and at length we replaced the staysail with a tiny storm jib. Under it we reached along at a good five knots till dark, when the wind increased still more and the barometer edged lower. Not knowing at what strength of wind and height of sea the little ship might find it difficult to round up, we decided to round up while we easily could. A night hove-to would do no harm, and I welcomed the chance to experiment with the ship in ocean seas. She came up smoothly, and showed us that in a moderate gale she'd lie comfortably under bare pole, about seven points off the wind. It was a useful thing to know. We left her that way for the night.

For two days, days in which we sailed mostly under storm sails, a strong wind rolled big seas endlessly eastward under a somber overhang. For me at least, those days were a revelation not entirely pleasant. The ship sailed beautifully, but in cold weather on the deep sea she seemed to lose the handiness which made her a joy to singlehand along the coast. Layers of heavy clothes with oilskins over them, plus the safety belts which each of us wore and kept snapped to the rigging, made bodily movement an effort. Trimming and changing sails was work, for there was a boom guy to trim as well as a mainsheet, and we had rigged downhauls on the headsails against the day or night when the wind might really whistle. Gimballing the stove had been part of our preparation, but with the ship moving fast in ocean seas it was hard to find places where cans and bowls would stay put. On a twenty-seven foot waterline a meal at sea is not just cooked. It has to be engineered.

Meanwhile no sun came through the clouds, and our track across the wind-streaked seas was lengthening. We began to wonder if Andy would get a fix before dead reckoning showed us near Bermuda's reefs.

We were five days out when the weather cleared and gave us another bright warm morning. At noon Andy caught the sun and vanished below to do his figuring. The wind had gone northeast and greatly moderated, and as we reached along under all sail with just an easy pitch and a cosy rustling at the bow two white birds, the first birds we'd seen, circled the masthead. Their long tails made them tropic birds. Bermuda had to be their base.

For fun I brought the RDF on deck, and as Andy emerged from the cabin with our position a voice came through the radio speaker, a voice advertising the price of lingerie in pence and shillings. Bermuda.

Andy's fix tallied with the radio bearing and put us a hundred and fifty miles northwest of the island. In the warmth and brilliance of the sunshine we grinned at each other, feeling we'd likely raise Bermuda the following day, our sixth day out. Fair enough for a crew of three!

But during that summery afternoon the breeze kept lightening, reminding us of the blow that a dying breeze had brought in before. For an hour the sails hung slack, and when a new air began to stir it came in from the south. Sailing over bright and merely rippled swells, we watched the headsails and played shifts of breeze as if racing in Long Island Sound.

Toward evening a steamer's bridge, high and cliff-like in the light of the westering sun, climbed over the southern horizon. Seeing us, the steamer altered course to pass close by. Half a mile to starboard she almost stopped, looking us over. Perhaps she knew what was cooking behind the haze gathering in the west. Satisfied we were shipshape, she put on speed and disappeared over the northern horizon.

As daylight faded from the ocean a southwest wind began humming in the shrouds. The glass started down. I decided to reef the main for the night, but in the short time taken to pull down a reef the wind's hum had risen to a whistle and the ship had heeled well over in a rising sea.

"We won't need the main at all," I hollered to Andy across a boom that had begun to jump. "Let's get the boom in the gallows."

Very quickly, as we secured the boom and darkness came, the force of the wind and the motion of the ship warned us that the night was full of gale. Hanging to the boom in a squall of rain, we decided to lower the staysail and hoist the trysail.

When Andy slacked the halyard the staysail tried to flog, but the downhaul brought it smartly down and clamped its luff to the plunging stem—completing my conversion to the downhaul school. Furling the soaked canvas and lashing it to the deck while wind and spray tried to tear it loose took time. Looking up from the job, it was good to see the trysail ready, brailed to a switch track on the mast.

Still, ready or not, there was the halyard to shackle on, a lashing to cast off, sheets to reeve through snatch blocks and lead to headsail winches, and finally the sail to hoist and trim—all in the dark with the deck jumping, the wind howling, and jets of spray thickening the rain. On that black and windy night we discovered the full value of a stout boom gallows and of safety belts for every man aboard.

Hove to under trysail on the starboard tack, the ship seemed steadier than under bare pole. For a while I held the wheel and squinted upward through the rain at the drum-tight sail and ahead where breaking crests glimmered in the darkness. The bow swung through an arc of about three points, but showed no inclination to come about. Satisfied, I lashed an anchor light to the boom. Working from handhold to handhold in the pitching, partly water-filled cockpit, I reached the scuttle and climbed below.

There was no reason to keep anyone on deck. One man dressed and awake below could stick his head out occasionally to see how the vessel rode.

"There's the spotlight," McVitty said, pointing to it, "and there's the Very pistol."

"Land," Andy pointed out, "is five hundred miles thataway."

"I mean for steamers," McVitty said.

So far so good, but the heel of the ship and her plunging, the rush of wind and seas in the darkness outside the hull, told us that this blow was already fiercer than the last. As we heated up a stew the barometer continued falling. Now was the time for shortcomings in the ship or in her fitting out to make their appearance, and they did.

Before we'd gone below, spray and occasional dollops of water had partly filled the cockpit—normal in heavy weather. Now, as the wind blew harder, heavier spray from bigger crests lashed the cabin house, and spray began coming through the companionway hatch in bursts, drenching the stove and galley. The stove performed heroically, but the galley became a mess, and of course the damp worked forward. A drip developed over the chart table. Another drip appeared below the skylight.

We had been pumping ship morning and evening, and twenty or thirty strokes had emptied her. This evening nearly a hundred were required. We decided to pump at each change of watch, but this did not prevent a pool of water forming on the lee side of the cabin sole and drearily sloshing back and forth. Where did this water come from? We bailed it with the bilge empty, but it returned. Crawling along the sole, chocking himself between bunks as the cabin pitched, Andy traced this water to a bilge bay forward and discovered that the bay had no limber hole at all. How the builder had overlooked the fact, how it had escaped me when I cleaned the bilge, I'll never know. There it was. Andy got a bucket and started bailing.

The gale kept building up, the barometer moving down. *Little Dipper* and I had ridden out a couple of hurricanes in sheltered anchorages, but now there was nothing to break the power of wind and sea, and the scream in the rigging was sounding more and more like the scream of Edna and Carol. Going forward on deck to see that everything was secure, I had to pull myself along the lifelines. Several times I was forced to stop and turn my face until gusts had passed. I could see little of the ocean—just a seething blackness marked by the gleam of breaking seas and foam.

Back in the splashing water in the cockpit, I hung to the try-sail sheets and looked out into the night. The thought came home that in all the hundreds of miles around us we could stay alive only in my ship's thirty-five feet of timbers and bent planking . . .

The ship maintained her heading, and for a few feet to windward, over the wet gleam of her rail, the water was smooth and black.

Our bunks stayed dry enough to be warm, and as the night wore on warmth became, to me at least, increasingly important. Probably fatigue had something to do with it, but when I stood —or sat—a watch below after midnight it seemed impossible to keep warm. My clothes were soaked and I'd run out of dry ones. As I got colder I got seasick, necessitating climbs into the half-filled, rain lashed cockpit, where I got wetter still and colder. Vicious circle.

The gale kept blowing harder. Occasional seas began to break through our windward smooth. Down in the cabin we could hear them coming. There'd be a seething sound off in the night outside the hull. The seethe would rapidly grow louder, become a roar, and then the cresting or breaking sea would smash like a sledge hammer against the topside. As this began to happen I mentally went through the operation of lowering sail and bending warps to cleats and samson post astern, and letting her scud off. We might have run before it from the start, but a November gale could easily blow three days. Bermuda lay not far to leeward.

Seethe—I heard one coming. Seethe growing louder, nearer. Roar—*Smash!* It seemed that that one must surely have broken up the dinghy, but, putting my head outside and probing forward with a flashlight, I saw the dinghy secure in its chocks and whole.

We found out later that this was the worst gale Bermuda had had for about a year. The weather station in Bermuda recorded a wind of sixty-five or better for some ten hours, with a peak of seventy-five. There is no reason to think that a hundred miles to the northward it was blowing any less.

When the ports and the plexi-glass in the scuttle turned gray with morning, the light filtering into the cabin picked out the details of that wretchedness which is a small boat's in a heavy gale. Now, as well as hearing and feeling the gale, we saw each other's dirty bearded faces, the wet and salt-caked oilskins and safety belts piled on a damp bunk aft, the sloshing pool of water on the cabin sole, dirty spoons and cups chocked in the tiny sink, damp blankets around damp men asleep. Upward, through the salt-stained glass in the scuttle, sheets of spray flew across the cockpit beneath the wet boom and the trysail's straining clew. Thick clouds raced overhead. The barometer was still edging downward. The gale showed no sign of moderating.

I clawed on one more layer of damp wool, buttoned oilskins over it, rigged a safety belt over that, and clambered into the cockpit for my first look from a little ship at a North Atlantic gale. The sight surprised as well as awed me. We rode no ocean that I had seen before. Instead of being hove-to on an ocean, surrounded by far away horizons, we seemed to hang precariously to a mountainside that fell off steeply to a bumpy valley. Instead of miles of water and a circling horizon, there was only the skyline of the mountainside we hung on, the valley below, and across the valley a jumble of foam-smeared foothills piling up to another mountainous crest. There was no view of distance —just the enormous seas enclosing us and above them a slice of dark gray sky.

A sea heaved us up and let us down, and we were higher on our mountainside, the valley deeper, but still enclosed by higher crests. Another sea got under us, and suddenly in a screaming gust of wind and spray we gained the top, and I glimpsed a whole sky, dark with clouds, from horizon to horizon across shaggy, foam-streaked miles of ocean. Then down we went into another valley, down and down with the sky narrowing above. Always heeling, pitching, whipped by cold spray.

Yet as I made my way below I felt re-assured. The seas were tremendous, but from their tops, during the glimpses I'd had of the ocean, I'd seen few whose breaking crests appeared high enough to sweep right over us. The ship was maintaining her heading and most of the time a windward smooth. Her hull was rugged. The rig looked secure. Watching the trysail's taut sheets and the iron-hard belly in its dacron cloth, it was good to remember that we had had the sail track through-bolted to the mast and that the sail was new.

"She's doing fine," I told the crew. "But the windward sheet will need some chafing gear. Sometimes it rubs against the boom."

When that job was done, I stood for a while in the cockpit to watch the ship. Heeled far over, her decks streaming with water and her lee rail often awash, she moved forward hardly at all. The trysail was behaving beautifully. The bag put in it by taking most of the pull on the windward sheet not only damped forward motion but prevented luffing when she swung toward the wind. But the broken foamy water at her bow and under her counter was visibly eddying. Despite her draft and generous forefoot she was making leeway fast. I estimated it at a knot and a half, and was not far wrong. The wind was northwest, blowing us toward Bermuda, but we had, I figured, over a hundred miles of sea room—enough to let us continue as we were for a couple of days if necessary, before having to scud off to avoid a lee shore and, if we could, beat back.

Below Andy was pulling on the pump. "She's taking plenty," he said.

"How many strokes so far?"

He grunted, "Hundred and forty."

It was quite a while before the pump sucked air.

We made tea and oatmeal, washed dishes and tidied up the cabin. After that there was little to do but roll into blankets and listen to the gale.

That afternoon I slept for two or three hours and woke up marvelously refreshed. Blinking upward through the glass in the forehatch, I saw a patch of blue sky. Hearing a wash of water past the planking at my ear, I thought for a moment that the gale had moderated and that my shipmates had her running for Bermuda, which could not be far away.

Then I saw sail bags piled on an after bunk and my shipmates crowded into the stowage space beneath the cockpit.

"We've found a leak," McVitty said.

Bermuda was as far away as ever, the gale still blew, and we had a leak. Oh, damn.

I rolled out and clambered aft.

Andy pointed at the pipe which led from the cockpit's lee scupper down to an opening in the hull. A film of water was rippling down the outside of the pipe. Its flange had lifted from the cockpit floor and half the water in the cockpit had been draining into the bilge.

By hammering packing up around the pipe McVitty stopped the leak.

When we backed out into the cabin I glanced at the barometer. Then looked again.

"Barometer's rising!" I said.

They crowded up to see.

An hour later, as night began to fall, the wind was screaming louder in the rigging, bursts of spray were again coming through the main hatch, seas had started to slam into us again, and the barometer was falling.

"Stonington," I murmured, "is a nice little town. A real nice town. Why did we ever leave it?"

At the moment no one had the answer.

The rest of that night, with shouting wind and heeling, pitching hull, repeated the night before. I remember chiefly the misery of an after-midnight watch, of having to roll out of a warm bunk, struggle into wet clothes and wet safety belt, and then sit up two hours in the dimly lighted cabin amid the smell of damp wool and stale air—feeling colder all the time, feeling sea-sickness coming, and feeling, as I pulled myself through the scuttle and hung my head across the cockpit coaming, utterly miserable. If an emergency had arisen, if the sail had split or the seas begun to comb, I doubtless would have found the energy to respond. But when my head hung over the cockpit coaming that seemed far from sure . . .

Finally that watch ended, and I crawled into my bunk and slept.

Some hours later I awoke, sleepily sensing that something strange was happening. The ship had lost her heel and was on her feet. The wind was blowing hard, but no longer howling. The trysail flogged—had it split?—and then the ship heeled over on the other tack. As I realized that she had come about, she was on her feet again, and with a smack of the sail she heeled over on the former tack. She'd come about, then jibed.

I rolled out, pulled back the hatch, and stuck my head outside. The night was black, but no spray was flying. The cockpit was almost empty. The wind had moderated. A flashlight showed sheets and sail secure. She'd gone back to her former heading.

"Barometer's been rising," Andy said.

At daylight the wind was east of north, and though the seas were huge they were long and regular, broken only on their crests. The sky was a low steely gray. The wind was strong, but the gale had ended.

After breakfast we took in the trysail, hoisted staysail and reefed main, and bore off southward at full hull speed. There was no hint of clearing in the sky, no hope of using a sextant, but the commercial radio in Bermuda came in strongly on the RDF. We had only to home on it, for we could expect to see Bermuda's hills—or more likely its lights—before we closed its northern reefs.

"If this wind holds," I guessed, "we ought to pick up Bermuda before midnight."

The wind held, veering just enough to make the staysail pull. The huge seas piling up astern, their crests growling as they overtook us and surged past, did not really worry us, but we treated them respectfully, holding her stern to them, then easing the helm as they dropped us into troughs. After being hove to, after taking what the sea dished out, it was exhilarating to have command of the ship again, to feel the weight and power of her forward rush. There was plenty of it. As she rolled, her shoulder dug up a roaring bow wave. All sheets were taut and straining. The wind pressed eagerly against the helmsman's neck. Behind him the log was humming. We ran hard and fast all day, averaging seven knots.

When darkness came we still were running fast and had sighted nothing. An hour later, the low sky hanging above the horizon ahead glowed faintly once, darkened, then glowed again. The loom of a light against the distant cloud cover became unmistakeable: Bermuda—that solitary lump of coral six hundred miles offshore!

We drove on, bringing the flash itself in view, then two more. North Rock, Gibbs Hill, St. David's Head, we figured—but which was which? Watching the flashes as the cockpit rolled, we tried to time them, but at each attempt the times seemed different. Then we remembered that the big seas overtaking us and lifting us up, letting us down, were also piling up in the darkness out ahead, now hiding the lights, then revealing them, falsifying the intervals between flashes. There was no way of telling what was an honest flash and what was not. And miles of reefs lay waiting to kill any ship that got too close.

"We'll harden up a bit," I said, "and hold off to the eastward. Then heave to for the night and go in tomorrow morning."

We were seven days and six hours out of Stonington.

That night we lay comfortably in moderating wind and sea with Bermuda's lights a few miles off our lee quarter. Meanwhile other lights, winking red and green ones, appeared overhead from time to time as newer, faster "ships" angled down through the clouds in search of Bermuda's airport. From New York, those "ships" were three hours out.

When Andy and I had hoisted sail the next morning and put her on the wind for St. David's Head, McVitty proudly handed plates of hot french toast and bacon up into the cockpit.

Mouth watering, I opined loudly, "Too bad he never learned to cook."

McVitty peered out anxiously from the scuttle.

"After you dropped this grub in the bilge," Andy said around a mouthful of it, "why did you stomp on it?"

"You clowns," McVitty said, "never had it so—"

Forward, there was a sudden loud report, and we saw a windward shroud fall overside.

Andy slacked the sheet and I jumped forward to drop the main.

Years earlier, I had saved money by accepting in place of independent lower shrouds one shroud looped around the mast, seized with wire, and from there led to the chain plates. Under the strain of the trysail, the wire seizing had bitten through the one-by-nineteen shroud. At the moment, although the sea was choppy, the mast seemed adequately supported by its intermediate and upper shrouds. For good luck we pulled down a reef. Neptune had been merciful.

We tacked up the Narrows and reached through Long Sound

*Bermuda News Bureau*

Hamilton. The Royal Bermuda Yacht Club in the foreground

toward Hamilton with sunshine brightening Bermuda's pink houses and their white stone roofs. We shucked off our woolens, washed and shaved, and toward dusk picked up a mooring off the Royal Bermuda Yacht Club.

Our first leg ended in that hospitable club's hospitable bar.

Wind moaned through the darkness outside my window at the club. A chop had made up in the harbor and was slapping loudly at the dock. Inside the room draughts played around my ears. Pulling the covers higher, I heard the wind get hold of a shutter and give it an angry shake. Moored off the dock for a departure the next day, *Little Dipper* was no doubt tugging at her mooring line.

Events at home had required my presence there and kept the ship in Bermuda for a month. During that time McVitty had left us. But now, thanks to Bert Darrell and his yard, we were ready to sail south. *Little Dipper* had new lower shrouds, a watertight hatch, proper limber holes. She was readier for sea than when we'd put Montauk astern, and we hoped we'd be sailing a gentler ocean.

"Wham—whammety—*wham!*" The wind had torn the shutter from one hinge and was flailing it against the building. Trysail weather still.

The following day we sailed around to St. George's, anchored off the quay, and I rowed ashore to telephone Dr. Mackey, the government meteorologist back in Hamilton. He had told me earlier that Bermuda was getting a series of low pressure areas whose winds began from the south, veered and strengthened, and finally went east of north and died away. If we caught one of these lows while it was blowing from the northwest, we might hope to ride it south beyond the latitude of winter gales.

Now he said over the phone, "I'm afraid this one won't last much longer. It may be followed by a calm."

I asked him if he had any dope on the next low. He said he

guessed it would not produce a gale. "Too bad you missed the northwest wind last night," he added. "It blew sixty!"

A real shame indeed.

"Mackey says it may go flat," I told Andy on returning to the ship. "But it's fair now. What do you say we shove?"

"Suits me."

With December more than half gone, it seemed wise to use sailable weather while we had it. During the previous winter, gales had beaten on Bermuda almost uninterruptedly, and a sizeable schooner bound from there to the Virgin Islands had disappeared at sea with all hands.

As we hove up the anchor dusk was falling and lights were coming on in houses ashore. We ghosted across the harbor and through narrow Town Cut. Outside, a northerly breeze filled the mainsail and stirred up a satisfactory rustle at the bow. Soon we had an ocean swell under us, stars overhead, and Gibbs Hill light dropping below a dark horizon.

By noon next day the breeze had died, and under a gray sky the ocean's shining surface was lumped and rounded as though by the backs of lolling whales. We lowered sail and set up both runners to prevent slatting, but the ship rolled and rolled. By evening both of us had had our heads across the rail.

As hazy stars came out and there was still no breeze, we wondered, none too cheerfully, what kind of low was heading for us from below the western horizon. Whatever kind it was, we evidently couldn't move without it.

Toward morning the air began to stir, and Dr. Mackey's educated guess proved accurate. This low was not severe.

Beginning with a southwest breeze and slowly veering, a free wind stayed with us for four days. And as those days went by, with all sails drawing and *Little Dipper* furrowing through the seas at five knots and often six, we "settled in" and the trip began to be enjoyable. When we'd left Bermuda the prospect of four hours on and four off, day after day, had seemed a little rugged. It didn't prove so, even though cooking and navigating shortened the four hours off. With another man aboard we'd have had more sleep, but now we had more room. This proved a surprising comfort. Cooking was simpler, and stowage was no problem. While we'd been in Bermuda, Dr. Joe Cunningham had blown in from Newfoundland singlehanded in a twenty-six footer. "Two men," he'd told us, "take more than twice the room of one. When I'm alone I can throw my gear anywhere."

Harry Pidgeon, it is said, solved the problem of stowing food by simply dumping cans in a heap on his cabin sole. When he got hungry he ate whatever was on top. "The problems of a singlehander," he reported, "are comparatively simple."

There's lots to be said for room.

The breeze was fresh and free, and *Little Dipper* loved it. Sometimes with both headsails helping the main, mostly with one, she kept the ocean foaming past her rail. Day and night she churned up a cheery bow wave. One night we saw the mast-head lights of two steamers simultaneously, both of them to port and hull down beyond the night horizon. Mysterious in their steady progress miles away, they held their courses across the darkened ocean. We held ours.

We were getting farther and farther south. Each night Orion, clearing the masthead with a night-long vault, vaulted higher in the sky. Each night Polaris shone lower on the backstay. We set no records, but came to count on a steady hundred and twenty-five miles each day. We got beyond the reach of winter gales, and one morning, when daylight revealed a flying fish on deck, we knew we'd passed the point where a dismasting would mean a long and weary drift to Europe. If we had to drift after sighting flying fish, we could drift toward the Bahamas. Fried for breakfast, that fish tasted swell.

By now the wind was in the north and lightening. We jibed over to put it on the quarter and to have some easting in hand when we reached the Trade. The wind lightened more, with the

air becoming noticeably damp and soft, and for twenty-four
hours we sailed slowly through the variables of the Horse Lati-
tudes, under and between fantastic piles of cloud. Some of these
strange clouds, though miles in area, had the shape of trees and
held their bulging "foliage" aloft on short thick "trunks."
Others were heaped into long gray cliffs astride the ocean, cliffs
streaming with high and wildly flaunted pennants. All one day
our course took us around or between these weird formations,
until at night the dark loom of one of them began to close on us
from the quarter. During most of the mid-watch I raced it,
profiting by the wind at its edge and watching over my shoulder
in the moonlight for the sudden oncoming of crowded whitecaps which accompany thunder squalls up north. During Andy's
watch it caught us. It had plenty of wind, but not enough to
make him think of reefing. As daylight brightened this cloud
broke up, leaving us in sunny weather with an easterly breeze
abeam: the Trade.

Two days and a night of perfect sailing followed, with the
ship reaching at a steady heel across seas too long to roll her. By
day these long blue seas glittered in brilliant sunshine, hour
after hour, while shoals of flying fish broke water off the bows
and fluffy little Trade Wind clouds paraded overhead. Sometimes a cloud darker than the others trailed a veil of rain across
the ocean, and after hours of tropic sunshine these brief rains
were welcome and refreshing. Our oilskins lay forgotten in the
cabin, along with woolen clothes, and we lifted our faces to
these showers and let the warm fresh water stream down our
bodies, washing salt away. By night more clouds sailed overhead with wide spaces of night sky between them, spaces lighted
by clear soft stars. And always, during that beautiful time, day
or night, the ship reached eagerly on, sailing in a wind that we
knew could not become a gale and had to stay abeam, a wind
that couldn't fail, a wind that had blown since Creation and
would blow free and fresh till Kingdom Come . . .

Mile after mile of rolling blue went bubbling past the rail, past the spinner of the log astern, and disappeared below a blue horizon. Now Bermuda lay many horizons back, beyond the Trade, beyond the variables, under colder skies in harsher weather, and mile by mile the question none of us had been able to answer earlier—why did we go to sea?—seemed to have a clearer answer. We had put Montauk hull down on a cold November evening. We had seen big ocean seas pile up astern. We and our ship had weathered a North Atlantic gale. Another gale would no doubt try her sometime, but we had gained experience that would make the next one easier. Now sunshine flashed along her shrouds, a warm wind filled her sails, and she sailed joyously toward tropic islands. "The ocean," said Josh Slocum, "is for men to sail on." Can anyone say more?

At four o'clock of a balmy Trade Wind morning, with the ship reeling off the miles and the Southern Cross hanging above the bowsprit, I leave the wheel and go below to shake up Andy.

"Now's your chance," I tell him.

A sleepy grunt: "What for?"

"You get to steer."

"Lucky me."

He also got to see the landfall. An hour after the sun had lighted up another brilliant tropic day, a faint blue speck appeared on the horizon off the port bow. Slowly it became a mountain top. When I came on deck at eight, more mountain tops had thrust their dim blue contours above the ocean's blue. There they were—the Caribbees, sentinels of Columbus' sea, combed by winds from Africa, warmed by unfailing sunshine.

Andy was frowning at the chart.

Puerto Rico, St. Thomas, Tortola, Virgin Gorda—the chart showed that all of them were mountainous. So were the smaller islands off them. During breakfast and afterward, as the ship went speeding on, we tried to identify the peaks that slowly rose and multiplied ahead. But no sooner would we find a shape that seemed to correspond to something on the chart than a further revelation left us as baffled as before. Andy broke out his sextant and waited on the cabin top for noon. We reached on, holding south, putting several distant peaks almost abeam to port.

At noon he got his sight and worked it out.

"Unless I've flubbed," he said, placing a finger on the chart, "we're right here."

"Right here" was five miles north of Savana Passage, the shortest route around St. Thomas to its harbor at Charlotte Amalie. He hadn't flubbed. We didn't alter course until within the Passage. From a departure eight hundred and fifty miles astern he had hit his target in the middle.

"Well," he said, "let's unfurl that Christmas pudding."

It was Christmas. We were eight days out.

Soon we smelled the land and were sailing past high brown cliffs and wooded mountainsides. We hardened up to make the harbor and the wind came briefly on the nose. We had to beat, but did so with the certainty that the warm wind blowing then would, come spring, be blowing fresh and fair along the coasts of Puerto Rico, Santo Domingo, Haiti, and along Bahama beaches all the way to Florida.

Beating for the harbor and the red roofed town, *Little Dipper* took it easy and chuckled in her bow wave. She could afford to. She had put a thousand miles of downhill Trade Wind sailing in the bank.

We felt good.

# CHAPTER III

## Coasting Along the Antilles

From the tip of Florida two chains of islands, the Bahamas and the Antilles, make out eastward into the Atlantic Ocean for about a thousand miles. Many of the Bahamas are little more than coral ledges, rarely visited by man, where only lizards hear the booming of the surf and remark the alternation of dazzling days and huge-starred nights. To the south, Puerto Rico, Hispaniola, and Cuba support teeming populations and stand up from the ocean in mountain masses rising as high as ten thousand feet.

The waters of this region vary too. On Bahama banks a boat can sail for days through clear green water, sighting only the tree tops of distant cays, while sand and ferns on the bottom are clearly visible two fathoms down. Yet in both the Bahamas and the Antilles a boat need only sail off a bank or through an opening in a reef to meet big blue Atlantic rollers—and maybe take a ton of water across her deck. The open ocean is a constant in these islands, and so, but for a rare calm or norther, is a boisterous Trade Wind. Not a gentle breeze, the Trade. At least not often. The Trade blows hard, always from the east, and makes the passage from Florida to this delectable region of the world a trying one even for big motorsailers.

But the passage west! For years, charts spread out in my apartment in Stonington, Connecticut, had made the passage from the Virgin Islands to Florida with the Trade off the quarter look pretty close to paradise for a man who cruises under sail. Finally one cold November evening my thirty-five foot cutter rounded Montauk and headed seaward for Bermuda, whence the course to the Virgin Islands would be due south, putting the Trade abeam. In sixteen days of sailing *Little Dipper* raised the Virgin Islands. In the spring of '56 she lay at anchor in St. Thomas ready for that passage west.

There would be, of course, what might seem drawbacks from some points of view. In the Antilles and Bahamas yacht yards are few and far between. Fresh meat and ice are obtainable only in the larger towns. Off Hispaniola and the remoter Bahamas buoyage leaves something to be desired. At night, lights shown on charts sometimes fail to shine. Except in Puerto Rico there is no Coast Guard, and a man who piles his vessel on a reef may lie there for a long, long time. Finally the Caribbean's bloody past and uneasy present scare many cruising men away from all but the biggest ports. (Today Castro scares any sensible man away from all Cuban ports.)

"Watch it," I was warned in St. Thomas, "when you get to Puerto Rico. Those Puerto Ricans like the knife!"

And, "The Dominicans are worse. You'd be smart to avoid them altogether!"

But charter skipper Shorty Meton, who of all sailors in St. Thomas knew the Antilles best—he'd cruised the Antilles often enough to make his own charts of anchorages, reefs, and currents —offered common sense instead of rumor.

"Go in hollering for service and your rights as an American," Shorty said, "and they'll strangle you with red tape. Act dumb and happy and everyone's your friend."

Would I have to observe laws about ports of entry in the various countries along my route, or could I cruise as in New England, anchoring anywhere?

"You can always claim an emergency," Shorty said. "You're sick or you need supplies."

But even Shorty admitted my ship should have some papers. Not being burdened with an engine, *Little Dipper* was not registered, so I visited the grocery owned by the Dominican Consul in St. Thomas and there bought a *despatcho* for the Dominican Republic. As is the way of *despatchos,* this one indicated that I'd sail direct to the Republic, which wasn't my intention. I let the matter ride and hoped the Dominicans would too.

*List of Arms.* Unsure whether I was wise or foolish, I filled out the form: "none."

*Crew List.* Edward Allcard has written that if you cannot find that rare bird, a perfect partner for a longish cruise, you are wise to cruise alone. That makes sense to me. So when the rare bird I'd lined up proved unable to make the trip, I turned down several pier-head volunteers. *Crew List,* therefore, me.

I had often singlehanded *Little Dipper* along the New England coast, but confess to wondering, as I hove up the anchor on a breezy morning in St. Thomas, if it was only a coincidence that I was shoving off for Florida on April Fools Day.

*Little Dipper* didn't seem to think so. Gusts off the harbor's hills filled her sails and she tacked smartly out the harbor entrance. Outside, a southerly slant to the Trade heeled her over and drove her, reaching fast, toward Puerto Rico's southern coast. Soon Puerto Rico's mountains were peering over the tops of the big blue seas rolling off to leeward. Jobos, seventy-five miles from St. Thomas, was the nearest harbor, but the roar of *Little Dipper*'s bow wave promised we'd be there for a whole night's sleep.

That promise failed. By noon the Trade had almost died, an extraordinary event. All afternoon we crept, inch by inch, across rounded swells with Monte Pirate on Vieques Island standing somber off the starboard bow against a bright hot sky. A mile or more ahead, a big cargo schooner flying the Dominican flag was only creeping, too. The sun went down in a crimson haze behind Puerto Rico's mountains.

When the night breeze came, northeast off the islands, it gave us one of those memorable sails which so often reward the man who cruises without an engine. An engine would have had me in Jobos, probably, asleep after a disappointing day. Now, with sheets well started, my belly full of supper, and a tea kettle swinging on the cabin stove, my little windjammer sailed past the lights of Jobos at a good four knots. She was moving too smoothly through too beautiful a night for me to think of stopping. The breeze picked up and we began to log five knots, with the sea rustling and whispering under enormous stars. At dawn, as we were rounding Muertos Island and standing in for Ponce, the gray light brightening over a rippled sea revealed our Dominican colleagues about a mile astern. *Little Dipper's* tall mast nodded placidly to my compliments.

The anchor had barely touched bottom off Ponce's handsome yacht club—the last we'd see—when a launch rounded up astern and offered me the club's hospitality.

*Little Dipper* lay in Ponce several days while I wandered about the city and rode through Puerto Rico's mountainous interior in crowded jitneys, called *publicos*. A Haitian consul in San Juan provided me with a *despatcho* for Cap Haitien. Despite my horrible attempts at Spanish, no one used a knife on me.

The morning we left Ponce the sun was brilliant and the Trade blew fresh out of the southeast. After reaching for some three miles' offing, we bore away for Cape Rojo at Puerto Rico's southeast corner and, around that cape, our next anchorage in Boqueron Bay. The sea was alive with flying fish, their blue bodies glittering in the sun, and the shoulders of the bare eroded mountains behind the coast shone golden in the dazzling light. With her boom guyed out *Little Dipper* romped along so rhythmically and easily that it came as a surprise to look astern and see that the translucent indigo seas rolling up behind the counter were seven and eight feet high. I was delighted to be sailing west.

By mid-afternoon we had jibed around Cape Rojo's orange-colored bluffs and were hard on the wind in a thunder squall

Cape Rojo—looking north

blowing down from the central mountains. Tacking toward Boqueron Bay in sharp gusts and driving rain, I was wondering if I'd be able to find the pass through a reef that guards the Bay before darkness fell, when the squall broke up and scattered westward over Mona Passage. The lurid glare of a sunset revealed a can buoy at the pass.

Morison states that Columbus used Boqueron Bay, and as *Little Dipper* tacked past the buoy in the day's last light I wondered how the Admiral of the Ocean Sea had worked his vessels in. No buoy helped him. He had no ship that tacked like mine. He must have drawn a good deal more than my six feet. Wherever you cross his track, you marvel at his seamanship.

Out of respect for mosquitos I put the anchor down half a mile off the mangroves that line the bay's circular shore. No mosquitos came to call. When I stuck my head out the cabin scuttle after supper, the bay and the shore were dark but for a few lights shining in a village a mile off at the head of the bay. From the village faint strains of *meringue* music floated across the smooth black water. A soft rain was falling. After the squally afternoon the anchorage felt snug . . .

Morning came off bright and still, and when I went on deck in the cool morning air I understood Shorty Meton's urging that I visit Boqueron Bay. *Little Dipper* lay motionless on a mile-wide mirror of green water bordered by the bushy green of mangroves and by palm trees glinting in the early light. Behind the palms and mangroves rolling fields of sugar cane were an even brighter green, checkered here and there by ploughed fields of vivid red. The village whose lights I'd seen was hard to find in daylight. Only a few houses stood in the cane fields. Rugged green hills rolled up behind the fields, and still farther off, still higher, mountains rose to a lofty skyline. Westward beyond the reef, Mona Passage glittered in a morning calm. Perhaps the fresh stillness of a morning after rain had much to do with it, but I thought then—and still think—that in all the

Americas there can be no anchorage more beautiful than Boqueron Bay.

A voice behind me startled me: "Good morning!"

Beach at head of Boqueron Bay

An undecked sloop I'd noticed earlier had caught a breath of air and silently come up astern. As the two Puerto Ricans in her reached for *Little Dipper*'s rail to hold the vessels apart, I saw the sloop's bilge was full of freshly caught red snappers.

After gamming with my visitors a while I asked them where they'd learned their English.

Both grinned widely in the shadows of their big straw hats. One said, "Harlem."

Harlem seemed a million miles away.

In a moment I demanded, "Why in *hell* would anyone who could live here pack up and go to Harlem?"

Their explanation was simple: they hadn't known what Harlem would be like. When they found out, they'd been able to save enough money to buy their passage home.

"We were lucky," one of them concluded. Smiling, he waved a hand at the green and tranquil bay and at the snappers in the sloop's bilge.

"Here's breakfast," the other one said as they shoved off. He tossed a plump fish on my deck.

There was little breeze that day—perhaps the rule along Puerto Rico's leeward coast—but a line of reefs offshore provides a kind of inland waterway in whose smooth water the lightest of airs will fan a ship along. We glided slowly toward Mayaguez, past a green shore backed by hills and distant mountains.

Another time I'll probably not lie at Mayaguez, for the anchorage was filthy, but now I saw a chance to put my *despatcho* for the Dominican Republic in order by a visit to Mayaguez' Dominican consul. Ashore I fell in with a Puerto Rican student who drove me to the consulate in his car. We failed, however, to find the consul in, and I returned to the ship planning an early start for what would be the longest jump of the trip: seventy miles across Mona Passage to Cape Engano, where there is no anchorage, and from there another seventy miles to Santa Barbara on Hispaniola's northern coast.

But as I was eating breakfast my student friend, concerned about what the Dominicans would do to me if my papers were not in order, rowed alongside and urged another trip to the consulate. His gesture was too friendly to refuse, but the trip again proved fruitless. It was noon by the time *Little Dipper* was underway.

A light air wafted us clear of Mayaguez and died. Then the ship lay becalmed, while smoke from a stack on Point Jiguero to the north streamed westward horizontally and whitecaps flashed on the northern horizon. The Trade was blowing, but not in Puerto Rico's lee.

Tidal currents crisscross through Mona Passage, and the Trade's habit of blowing onshore in daytime along both the Atlantic and Caribbean coasts of Puerto Rico sets up cross swells in the passage. During most of the afternoon light airs kept *Little Dipper* wallowing slowly through this cross swell while Desecheo Island, a barren yellow mountain, slowly materialized out of the sunlit haze ahead. By 1700 Desecheo came abeam, some miles to the north, and I got a fix by crossing its bearing with that of the San Francisco Hills near Mayaguez. Then the breeze died utterly.

*Little Dipper* rolled. She pitched. She slatted. I lowered the main and lashed the boom in the gallows, and the ship rolled more, pitched worse, and wallowed indescribably. She had been in uneasy calms before, but never in one approaching this. All around her the sea was heaped up in pyramids and spouts and ridges, each one high and steep. Similar seas sometimes get up in the Race at the end of Long Island Sound, but only when a strong wind bucks the current. Here, no wind stirred, and when I could read the bearing of the San Francisco Hills on the wildly swinging compass that bearing indicated little drift. But *Little Dipper*—ordinarily an easy-motioned vessel—jumped and bucked so violently that it would have been risking injury to sit on the lazarette behind the wheel. Even crouching on the cockpit floor there was danger of being tossed bodily overside. Thankful for my safety belt, I kept it snapped to a lifeline, and hung on tight.

As evening came the motion worsened. Seas began slopping across the rail and over the cockpit coaming. A pool of water inches deep sloshed around the cockpit floor. *Little Dipper* had weathered gales offshore, but I doubt if anything had ever tried her rigging as did that Mona Passage calm. Grovelling in the cockpit's steadily replenished pool of water, and watching my mast's wild gyrations against the sky, I wondered how long the chain plate fastenings would keep the mast in the boat. An engine would have helped, although in that sea a propeller would have been out of water as much as in it.

Finally, as the sun began to set, clouds that had been thickening over Puerto Rico all afternoon loosed their hold upon its mountains and drifted down upon my floundering vessel. By dark the sky was overcast and rain was falling. A breeze out of the northeast filled the staysail, and, still wallowing horribly, *Little Dipper* gained steerage way.

For an hour or more, not wanting to ruin the main with slatting, and far from sure that I could hoist it with the ship rolling, stumbling, and staggering as she was, I sailed—or floundered—through a black night under staysail only. At length the breeze began to freshen. Working from handhold to handhold along the deck, I crawled forward on all fours to the mast. Arrived at the mast, I had to embrace it with both arms before I dared stand up, and then I saw that I wouldn't be able to haul on a halyard too. Everything counselled the posture of prayer, so I dropped to my knees again and on my knees managed to hoist the main without fouling anything. Breathing benediction on the sailmaker who had advised a mainsail cut without headboard, roach, or battens, I crawled aft.

Now, for the first time that day, *Little Dipper* began to move. I laid a course from my afternoon fix to pass five miles north of Cape Engano, and streamed the log. Soon we were rolling along at a good six knots. By 2200 we had the loom of Mona Island light abeam to port and were ramping along at seven knots, still rolling, with the seas rising before a strengthening wind and snarling and growling as they came out of the darkness off the quarter.

Although the chart called Cape Engano's light "unreliable," the light's flashes appeared an hour or two after midnight, far ahead in a blackness without horizon. The flashes were off the starboard bow, indicating a strong southerly set in the Passage. I hardened up to make more northing, and the vessel picked up speed and steadied. The breeze held fresh out of the northeast, and the stars began to shine between low clouds. Shortly after 0300 Cape Engano was abeam. A bow and beam bearing told me that we were six miles off and still tearing through the darkness at seven knots.

Some ten miles beyond Cape Engano, Point Macao thrusts its rocky head half a mile to sea and offers a reef-protected anchorage. But the entrance is not marked, and it seemed a shame not to make the most of what an increasingly starry sky promised would be a fine Trade Wind day. I ran on, keeping my offing, until the sky astern paled with dawn. Then I hove to on the offshore tack for a brief sleep and a bowl of oatmeal and sugar.

We ran fast along the Dominican coast all day before a pressing Trade, with the sea between white tumbling crests so deep an indigo that it was almost purple. By early afternoon Mount Diablo at the entrance to Samana Bay came up over the horizon, and at 1700 we were running between its steep green shoulder, planted with rows of coconut palms, and jungly Levantado Cay. The chart called the buoys in Samana Bay "unreliable," and I failed to sight a charted bell, but other buoys appeared as shown. I rounded up at one of them, took in the staysail, hoisted the yellow flag, and readied the anchor. Under mainsail only we bore away for the narrow entrance to the harbor at Santa Barbara.

"Like as not," the captain of a big diesel yacht had warned me in St. Thomas, "the Dominicans will say "hello" with a shot across your bow."

"They're a bloody people," my friend in Mayaguez had said.

The ex-Harlemites in Boqueron Bay had warned me to expect the worst.

Santa Barbara

Trujillo gunboat at Santa Barbara

Travelling fast before the Trade, *Little Dipper* was threading a narrow passage between a high green mountainside and a high green cay when I saw, a cable length ahead, the snout of a P.C. boat jutting out from the cay's lush foliage. The P.C.'s stern was evidently moored to the shore. Her deck gun was pointed between my eyes.

Ploughing up bow waves port and starboard, I held my course. As the harbor opened up and the houses of Santa Barbara appeared to starboard, a burly black man dressed in naval sun-tans stepped into the P.C.'s bow and waved me toward him. I jibed over and luffed up to him. When I pointed at myself and hollered "St. Thomas!" he waved me on.

A string of cays parallel to the shore formed Santa Barbara's harbor, and the town's houses, red-roofed and painted pink and green and blue, climbed from the water toward a green hilltop dominated by an old stone fortress. I anchored where the chart promised room to swing. The anchor was barely down before a crowded launch put out from the shore and came alongside.

Seven officials, no less, scrambled aboard. But all were smiling and one spoke English. Their friendliness was evident. I put glasses and a whiskey bottle on the cabin table.

Not much more than a village, Santa Barbara was the prettiest town I'd seen so far. I lay in the harbor several days, often wishing that I spoke enough Spanish to talk to the teen-agers who rowed out to gaze at me.

I spent two days on a trip across the island by *publico* to Ciudad Trujillo. That capital differs little from any other, and it seemed to me that the real character of the Dominican Republic emerged in its cane fields and villages, along its coasts and on its mountain roads. There the Dominicans were often impoverished peasants, sometimes pistol-toting, horseback riding *caballeros*, courteous, violent, intensely Spanish. Trujillo—or as one sees his name written everywhere—Generalissimo Doctor Raphael Leonidas Trujillo Molinas, Benefactor de la Patria—ruled the country with his army, but his army seemed for the most part disciplined and soldierly. In one respect Trujillo's system suited me: *Little Dipper* lay unattended, hatches open, off Santa Barbara for three days, and nothing aboard her was touched.

"We have a place for robbers," the Commander of the Port had assured me. The place was the stone fortress on the hill. I climbed up to it on a Sunday and found its cells thrown open and its courtyard jammed with a noisy crowd of prisoners and prisoner's wives and children. Returning toward the harbor, I fell in with a crowd of men and boys headed for the local cockpit. Judging by the hush that preceded each fight and by the gambling and yells accompanying them, the fights were good ones. But the action was too fast for my eye to follow. All I saw were sudden flurries of feet and feathers.

When I applied for a *despatcho* the Commander was somewhat put out to learn that I'd made my trip across the island without a travel permit from him. I had done so out of ignorance, and when the *publico* in which I rode had stopped at army checkpoints, where soldiers inspected papers, I kept up appearances by showing a hometown library card. It had been scrutinized and returned without complaint.

From Santa Barbara *Little Dipper* had to beat back eastward to get clear of Samana Bay, but we did so in the morning before the Trade had freshened. Once clear, we were able to lay a northeast course for Cape Samana. As we reached northeast that Cape came grandly out of the sea. When it lay a mile to port it seemed to tower over us. Flat-sided and flat-topped, it was an enormous red stone cliff, eight hundred feet high and ten miles long. Sheer and cleanly squared, this colossal cliff seemed less a work of nature than a rampart constructed against the Atlantic by some vanished race of giants.

For an hour or two this cliff seemed to touch the limit of the spectacular, and then the ship's progress through hurrying beam

seas opened up the still more awesome cliffs and mountains of
Cape Cabron. The Trade's moist atmosphere makes things at
any distance look dim and far away, and so no doubt increases
the apparent size and height of mountains. Still, the mountains
of Cape Cabron do rise more than twice as high as the red cliff
of Cape Samana, and the seaward buttresses of these mountains,
too, are cut off sheer and clean. They front the Atlantic with
more huge cliffs, gouged at their base by caverns into which
the ocean's long swells roll, exploding in geysers and thunder-
ing like the fire of heavy guns. Seen across a dazzle of whitecaps
and blue sea, these cliffs and geysers and the hazy green mountains above them lured me in as close as I dared go. Rounding
Cape Cabron with *Little Dipper* running fast before the eager
Trade, I saw a tremendous natural bridge joining two of those
geysered cliffs. Beyond the shadow hanging from that bridge,
sunshine lighted up a giant ampitheater walled by mountains.

Bound for "Port Escondido," an uninhabited bight in what
I thought would prove the lee of Cape Cabron, *Little Dipper*
held a fair wind for several miles under a mountain that rose
eighteen hundred feet, too steep for trees, from Cabron's western shore. We were halfway along this mountain's base and
running fast when taken aback by a strong wind from dead
ahead. I cast off the boom guy and hardened sheets, and for an
hour we were hard on the wind and tacking. Overhead, Trade
Wind clouds sailed serenely westward across a soft blue sky, but
our wind came furiously from the bight ahead. Entering the
bight, *Little Dipper* had her rail under and water streaming
through her turnbuckles.

The chart showed a three fathom depth close inshore, but for
some time after dousing the staysail and readying the anchor I
could find no bottom at all. Heaving the lead, I tacked and
circled in violent gusts and gingerly edged nearer to a beach on
which big combers were crashing in a haze of windblown spray.
After half an hour of this a negro emerged from the brush be-

hind the beach and pointed to a spot still further in. Following his directions, I found bottom in three fathoms and put the anchor down.

Cabron's mountains made the anchorage spectacular. At dark, swarms of fireflies soared up against the mountains' high black profiles. But my appreciation of the place was checked by the combers' ceaseless thunder on the beach and by thought of what a trap that bight would be in winds from the northwest. The ship rolled and pitched in the surge. A hard wind blew off the beach all night.

Next morning, a skiff rowed by the negro of the day before came alongside, carrying a sombrero'd white man who wore a cartridge belt and pistol. The negro questioned me in English, the white man made notes in a notebook, and they put off for shore. After dragging the skiff clear of the breakers on the beach, they vanished into the brush. I saw no sign of human habitation.

Fifteen miles to the west of Escondido, Port Jackson offered a good anchorage behind a reef, but feeling sure of the Trade I shaped a course around Cape Viejo Francis for Puerto Plata, eighty miles away. A light breeze gave us a lazy morning sail across swells that were only rippled. Toward afternoon the breeze freshened, *Little Dipper* started making knots, and it looked as though we'd reach Puerto Plata before the following dawn. Aeolus, however had other plans. I was not to see Puerto Plata for days.

When the mountains behind Cape Viejo Francis rose above the sea that afternoon and the low land of the Cape itself came into view, clouds were thickening over them. I hardened up to stand away to seaward of what looked like a local thunderstorm, but by 1600 the sky over the ocean, too, had darkened. Although an easterly breeze continued blowing, it seemed prudent to take in the masthead jib.

As I was completing a bow and beam bearing to get my distance off the Cape, a squall struck us from dead ahead. For several minutes *Little Dipper* was hard on the wind with rain and spray flying and her mast well over. Then the squall passed. Rumbling with thunder and lit by lightning flashes, it drifted eastward toward Cabron over a dull gray sea. I hoped that was the end of it—though its eastward drift was ominous. Fifty miles still lay between us and sleep in harbor.

Another squall struck, and after it another. For two hours squall after squall, each blowing from the northwest, alternated with flat calms in which the ship rolled, sails slatting, under a gloomy sky with the dim shape of Cape Viejo Francis now upwind. At length, as the dark afternoon grew darker still with evening, a strong nor'wester began to whistle across the tops of rising seas. Although it was April and we were hundreds of miles to the east of Florida, a standard Norther had come in. Its westerly slant made it a dead muzzler on my course around the Cape.

A winter in the Caribbean had accustomed me to the Trade. I expected easterly winds as my inalienable right and would put up with nothing else. Mildly cussing the Norther, but confident that in April it could not last long, I hove to on the offshore tack under reefed main and backed staysail, and went below. Windward work in the open ocean had never been my idea of pleasure anyway. Why punish self and ship with a beat to windward when, once the Trade resumed, we'd have an easy run to port? I cooked supper and turned in.

At dawn, to my disgust, big seas still rolled down upon us from a gray horizon. The wind still blew strong and cold out of the northwest. And with the sail I'd left hoisted the ship had drifted far to leeward. Cape Viejo Francis now was out of sight ahead. The low clouds racing over the roughened sea gave no sign of breaking up.

All morning *Little Dipper* slugged her way to windward, but by noon, although we had logged twenty-five miles, we still were

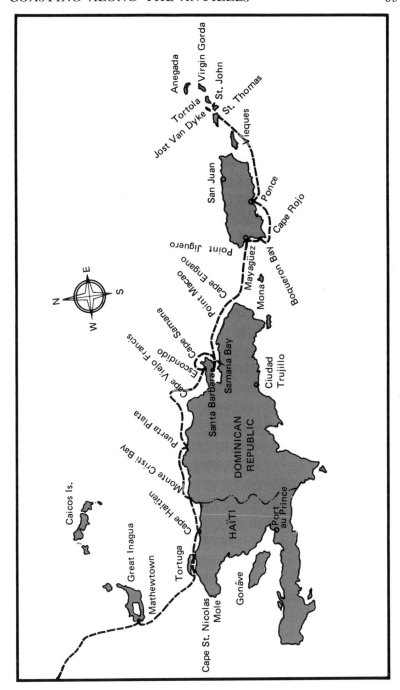

not around Cape Viejo Francis. The Norther had built up steep and shaggy seas, and to keep my little vessel driving through them I had to lay her more than five points off the wind. Tacking inshore until I saw the Cape, I would make some six points to the westward, but on the offshore tack I had to head two points to the east of north, sailing away from my ultimate destination. By noon I was cold and wet inside my oilskins and increasingly disgusted. My cussing sharpened.

The alternatives remained the same. I could give the ship and myself a beating, trying to get to windward against the Norther, or heave to and wait for justice in the form of sunshine and the Trade. By midafternoon I was experimenting with the vessel, trying to find a trim of the sails that would keep her going to windward, however slowly, without my help. Trimming the staysail amidships turned the trick. I lashed the helm and for an hour watched her sail herself offshore on a heading closer than I could sail her. At dark, back sights on the light at Cape Viejo Francis showed we were making very little leeway. According to the log we were moving through the water at better than two knots.

The ship was happy, but I was not. Her motion did not seem violent, but I didn't feel like eating. Before turning in I had to hang my head across the rail. Although rough seas and fatigue surely contributed to this fit of seasickness, my mental attitude was probably the chief cause. A continuing head wind in those waters at that time of year seemed cruel, unusual, and, I guess, against God. I felt that I'd been jobbed.

I turned in with the notion of raising chickens somewhere out in Kansas.

A good night's sleep, interrupted once to go on deck and tack ship, worked wonders. At dawn the wind still blew from the northwest and seas still were big, but the gray blur of the mountains behind Cape Viejo Francis, itself below the horizon, bore due south. We had sufficient offing to hope to clear the next cape on the inshore tack.

As if rewarding a stouter frame of mind, the wind began to moderate and veer. By ten o'clock the sky had cleared, the boom was guyed out to a light Trade off the quarter, and the sea was again a tropic blue. Not long after noon the profile of Loma Isabella de Torres, a conspicuously flat-topped mountain, rose above the horizon some twenty miles ahead. Puerto Plata lay beneath it, and after some hour's running *Little Dipper* was standing in for the harbor entrance. The town's red roofs and the yellow towers of its cathedral made a handsome picture under the dark green mountain.

Much larger than Santa Barbara, Puerto Plata proved equally hospitable. I lay there several days, making acquaintances ashore and relying on the good nature of Ricardo Limardo, the English-speaking Immigration Officer, to smooth my way through officialdom's red tape. Among the people I met was Abraham Smith, boss of a warehouse on the quays. A big, jet black Turks Islander with a voice like a 155 howitzer, Smith had skippered schooners along that coast for twenty years. When I remarked that harbors seemed few and far between, he boomed, "Mon, all you gotta do 'most anywhere is get in behind d'reefs!" But he admitted that it might be wise to make your first trip in with someone who knew the entrances, which are not marked.

Turks Islanders seem outstanding anywhere you meet them. Lacking opportunity on their barren island, they have settled all over Hispaniola and most of them have prospered. Yet, like Abraham Smith, nearly all of them resist pressure to change their citizenship and remain proud subjects of Her Majesty the Queen. She might, it seems to an outsider, preserve a valuable resource for the Commonwealth if she persuaded Turks Islanders to live somewhere in it.

Smith named the Hotel Madrid as the best place in town for meals. It fronts the cathedral plaza, and from its dining room,

open to the plaza, I watched the beauty and chivalry of Puerto
Plata parade each day at dusk according to age-old custom:
groups of young men sauntering around the plaza clockwise,
groups of girls counter-clockwise, while from surrounding
benches older folk carefully watched the brief flirtations. When
the sun was high the plaza lay deserted, even its palm trees seeming overcome with heat, while in the siesta silence the Atlantic
thundered tirelessly on outlying reefs.

The Trade blew hard while I lay in Puerto Plata. The burly
Puerto Rican skipper of a diesel-powered workboat bound eastward from Miami to Antigua came close to crying on my
shoulder as he told of the trials he'd had in the Trade's head
seas. His American engineer sorrowfully corroborated his tale.
I had made my easting between Montauk and Bermuda, and
plan to do the same again. The only practical alternative to this
outside route for a sailing vessel seems to be to work the Trade's
slants through the Bahamas to, say, Rum Cay or San Salvador,
and wait there for a Norther. With luck, a strong Norther in the
fall might then carry a sailing vessel eastward to where she
could lay St. Thomas across the Trade.

Now *Little Dipper* had the Trade astern. When she sailed out
of Puerto Plata the Trade picked her up and made her fly. She
easily ran the sixty miles to the smooth water of Monte Cristi
Bay by nightfall. There, sailors from another of the P.C. boats
that guard Trujillo's coasts boarded me. My *despatcho* named
Cap Haitien as my next port after Puerto Plata, but these watch
dogs—after sampling my whiskey and my supper—let me lie.
They added their voices to ones I'd heard in Puerto Plata
warning me of the perfidy of Haitians.

Morning came off bright and calm. For several hours we did
no more than ghost through glassy water among the sandy cays
to the west of Monte Cristi. As we ghosted, big fish began jumping all around the ship. I threw over a lure, and a fish hit it
and leaped ten feet in the air while I was still paying out the

line. He didn't have to run. The force of his strike parted my line. I tried another lure, and the same thing happened. I didn't know what kind of fish these were, but guessed king mackerel. They were four or five feet long.

Toward afternoon the Trade picked up and drove us through flashing whitecaps toward Cap Haitien's high green mountains. *Little Dipper* jibed around the buoy off Picolet Point at close to hull speed and stormed up the harbor before a wind that blew like Billy-O. A long pier with a warehouse on it juts into the harbor, and a score of native sloops were moored to the pier's lee side. I rounded up to swinging distance off it and put the anchor down. The main was barely furled when a dozen port officials and assistants came out in a launch. My French proved comprehensible to them—as did my cigarettes and booze.

In Haiti, they admitted, an unattended boat required a watchman. A hail to the shore brought out a candidate for the job. Lean and hungry-looking, unshaven, villainous of eye, Rafael Charles seemed cast for the role of Minor Pirate; not a Long John Silver, not a brawling Billy Bones, but a skulking pirate, a slit-your-throat-at-night pirate, above all a petty thieving pirate. But Rafael Charles proved boundlessly conscientious and possessed of the integrity one hopes for in Supreme Court judges.

With Rafael installed aboard the ship, I took a room at the completely charming Hostellerie du Roy Christophe, and for two days enjoyed its luxurious combination of the tropics and provincial France.

French in language and in the look of the shuttered stucco houses along its narrow streets, and French in the food served at the Hostellerie, Cap Haitien contrasted strongly with what I'd seen of the Dominican Republic. Judging by the books in its bookstore, Cap Haitien supports a cultivated society. On the other hand, signs of poverty were unmistakeable. A trip to Henri Christophe's *citadelle* drove home a remark heard about

Haitian farmers being killed by falling out of corn fields: inland of Cap Haitien you see ragged men and women using
crowbars and machetes to cultivate tiny fields of maize on mountainsides far too steep for ploughs.

The *citadelle* itself, its grim and lofty walls standing straight
up from a mountain peak, deserves a place in any list of wonders
of the world. That an ex-slave conceived it and somehow got its
huge stones and heavy cannon dragged up to that fantastic peak
and there shaped and fitted into place suggests the kind of
slavery he had known—and resolved never to know again. On
the lowland below that soaring fortress, only mouldering walls
remain of Christophe's palace, but their extent indicates a
building on the same scale as Versailles.

Although Haiti, like the Dominican Republic, was ruled by
force, Haiti's government seemed less military than Trujillo's
and less efficient. Back in St. Thomas, Shorty Meton had advised
me to avoid the splendid natural harbor at the western tip of
Haiti, Cape St. Nicholas Mole. There, a year or two earlier,
Shorty had stood off piratical "officials" by laying his Win-
chester across his bulwark. Now, the friendly officials in Cap
Haitien echoed Shorty's advice. It seemed that many of the
coastal towns were connected with the rest of the country only
by sea and that the control of the central government over those
towns was loose at best. Along this coast the spirit of piracy roots
deep. Tortuga Island bred the buccanneers. The brotherhood
of the Sea was founded at Port a l'Ecu.

I paid off Rafael one evening and passed a hot and windless
night trying to sleep on *Little Dipper's* deck. A Turks Island
sloop was anchored near. For her, home lay a hundred and
twenty miles to the northeast, to windward against the Trade.
That afternoon her skipper had told me that the night breeze off
the mountains often carried him thirty miles to sea, and now he
was impatient for the night breeze to rise. His voice and the
voices of his crew, all of them grouped around a pile of embers

on the old sloop's deck, sounded clearly in the quiet darkness.

"Skippah," a soft voice soothed him, "we jus' gotta wait for de wind."

No doubt the same words had sounded in Ulysses' ears, in Greek.

When I awoke at dawn, the sloop had vanished.

The land breeze wafted us down the harbor in the cool of the morning, but failed a mile or two offshore. Before the Trade got up, we lay becalmed.

That afternoon the Trade gave us a splendid run along the Haitian coast and between the mountains on either side of Tortuga Channel. Native sloops were all about. I must have counted fifty, plus two or three big schooners. By nightfall we were off the western point of Tortuga Island, and it appeared that a quiet anchorage might be found under that point's lee. With headsails furled and anchor ready I luffed cautiously inshore by moonlight, toward a beach in a shallow bight. As I worked in, watching for coral heads, the color of the water beneath the ship changed suddenly to ghostly white—the bottom! I hove the lead. It sank in thirty feet. Only in the Virgin Islands had I encountered water so clear. I held on slowly, heaving the lead, and found a quiet anchorage in twenty feet, hard sand.

Despite dire warnings from the Haitians that the Cubans would in all probability relieve me of both boat and life, (today of course, Castro might), my *despatcho* named the Cuban port of Baracoa as my destination. Actually I hadn't decided which of two possible routes to Florida I would sail. Cuba and the fine natural harbors on its northern coast looked inviting on the chart, but visiting them would leave me with a jump of more than two hundred miles in the steamer-infested Straits of Florida, a long jump for a singlehander who likes occasionally to sleep. It was, I'd been told by a man who had done it, possible to avoid the steamer routes by sailing from midway along the

Cuban coast straight across the Grand Bahama Bank, where in
ordinary weather you can anchor anywhere, to Orange Cay
south of Bimini. But one man's success in navigating uncharted
shoals in unpredictable currents does not guarantee another's.

The alternative was to sail from Tortuga to Great Inagua
and up through the Crooked Island Passage to Long Island, the
Exumas, and Nassau. This route would let me visit remote
Bahama Islands, but here, too, harbors were few and far between. From my anchorage under Tortuga, Great Inagua was
seventy miles to the northwest and offered only an open roadstead, untenable in a Norther. Eighty miles further on, Castle
Island offered little more.

Next morning the Trade made up my mind. It was blowing
hard, gusting even in the lee I'd found. Beyond the low finger
of coral that was Tortuga's western tip, big seas were rolling
in the Windward Passage. The horizon northward was jagged
with broken crests and whitecaps. Such wind promised a fast
reach to Great Inagua, and a weather report on the Nassau radio—the first report I'd had, though doubtless many had been
on the air in Spanish—made no mention of a Norther. I tied
in a reef, gammed a while with a boatload of Tortuga fishermen,
and by 0900 had the vessel out in the swing of the seas and going
like a flying fish for Great Inagua.

# CHAPTER IV

## *Through the Bahamas*

Bound from Haiti to the Bahamas, *Little Dipper* was getting a strong dose of what the Bahamas usually offer: wind. Haiti's mountains were sinking fast into a tumble of seas astern, and a boisterous Trade was creaming the tops of big gray rollers coming up on the starboard beam under a cloudy sky. Carrying only staysail and reefed main, lifted up and partly out of the water as crests rolled under her, my little ship was logging better than eight knots.

She loved that fast beam reach, and for several hours of the April morning I loved it too. But there's no denying that a man beam-reaching in a little ship across big ocean seas gets swung like a cat by the tail. As *Little Dipper* rose to the charging crests and they tossed her toward the sky, I tightened my grip on the wheel and hung on, waiting for her to drop back down into her native element. Down she dropped, but found that element lower by several feet than when she'd left it. She rolled, dipped her rail in the broken water racing past, and not only on the crests of those beam seas but in the chop between them the ocean slopped over the cockpit coaming into my pants' pockets.

By noon my arms were weary with hanging on and under my oilskins I was wet and shivering. It seemed more like an October day off Montauk than April in the tropics.

Although the wind moderated in the afternoon, *Little Dipper* sailed the seventy miles from Tortuga Island to Great Inagua at an average speed of more than seven knots. That's good going on a twenty-seven foot waterline, but when I had her stay-sail furled and was tacking inshore toward Mathewtown at dusk, I felt as if I'd gone three rounds with Rocky Marciano.

I was swinging the lead and had found bottom at four fathoms when a voice hollered from the darkening shore: "Let 'er go!"

*Bahama News Bureau*

Mathewtown Light, Great Inagua

It was too dark to see the voice's owner, but, assuming he knew whereof he spoke, I put the anchor down.

Fresh from Haiti and the Dominican Republic, I expected to see a launch come out of the darkness bearing a crowd of officials eager to read my papers and sample my cigarettes and booze before they'd let me rest.

Water lapped the hull. Lights shone in houses ashore. No launch appeared. Then I realized that I had sailed into British waters and that the British Commonwealth sees no great threat to its security in the arrival off its shores of one small sailing vessel. It was going to let me have what I most wanted, peace.

I brewed a cup of tea, spiked it with a jolt of rum, and raised the cup toward the lighted shore: "Gentlemen—the Queen!"

Morning came off hot and still. Sunshine flashed on the roadstead's green water, and the beach and houses of Mathewtown were dazzling white under a hot blue sky. I called on the Commissioner, who waived my lack of a proper *despatcho* and gave me the Transire which allows a cruising boat to sail and anchor anywhere in the Bahamas. Ice and groceries proved available, and a visit to the office of the salt works developed the information that a sailing vessel can find an anchorage secure from Northers in South Bay not far from Mathewtown. The entrance to this anchorage can be seen on H.O. Chart 948 where the chart shows six fathoms.

While I lay off Mathewtown lack of wind for the eighty mile jump to Castle Island seemed more likely than a Norther. Fluffy Trade Wind clouds sailed over *Little Dipper*'s masthead, but sailed slowly. The day I left, I got the anchor up at 0600 and cooked breakfast while reaching past Middle Point under both headsails and the main. Turks Islanders with whom I'd talked at Cap Haitien had told me that Hogsty Reef, a few miles east of the course from Mathewtown to Castle Island, was easy to enter and a good anchorage, and I thought I might stop there. A two mile wide lagoon in the Atlantic, a lagoon circled by tiny cays and coral heads, Hogsty Reef must surely be one of the wildest and loneliest anchorages in the Americas. A night at anchor there would be a night to remember. But as *Little Dipper* reached across the sea's deep blue she gradually took more heel and the rustle at her bow strengthened to a steady snoring. Soon she was logging better than six knots. Regretfully, but wanting to make the most of a perfect sailing day, I held on for Castle Island.

Approaching that island, I was able to check my course by the masts and superstructures of steamers, hull-down to port, entering and leaving Crooked Island passage. This traffic warned me of a westward set—which can pile a vessel up on the Miro Por Vos ("Look Out For Yourself!") rocks—and I hardened up two hours before the high tower of Castle Island light came over the horizon. By evening we were around Castle Island and north of it, tacking inshore and heaving the lead to find an anchorage in Jamaica Bay. In a little over twelve hours *Little Dipper* had sailed more than ninety miles, averaging the same speed as from Tortuga to Great Inagua, but this time under all sail and in such easy going that when my cap blew overside that afternoon rounding up to retrieve it was no labor.

I found an excellent anchorage close inshore with Salina Point on Acklin's Island bearing NNW. When the anchor had taken hold in the sandy bottom and the ship lay quiet in smooth water, I saw no sign of mankind anywhere. The stillness and the enormous sky above the beach bespoke the remoteness of these islands.

When I went on deck after supper, the moon had risen and the bay and the beach were bright with moonlight. Over the ship's side, starfish and lumps of coral were clearly visible on the bottom. The ship slowly rose and settled as an occasional swell invaded the bay and died on the moonlit beach in a liquid rustle. From the shore came the calls of land birds, a

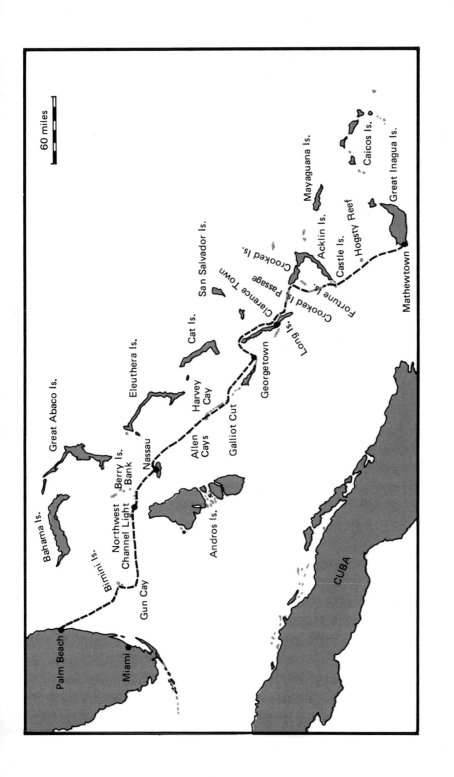

60 miles

Palm Beach
Miami

Bahama Is.

Bimini Is.

Gun Cay

Northwest
Channel Light
Berry Is.
Bank

Nassau

Great Abaco Is.

Eleuthera Is.

Andros Is.

Allen
Cays

Galliot Cut

Harvey
Cay

Cat Is.

San Salvador Is.

Georgetown

Clarence Town

Long Is.

Crooked Is. Passage

Fortune Is.

Crooked Is.

Castle Is.
Hogsty Reef

Acklin Is.

Mayaguana Is.

Caicos Is.

Great Inagua Is.

Mathewtown

CUBA

sound that always seems the final satisfying touch to a long day spent at sea. For an hour or more I sat in the cockpit, enjoying the night, and giving thanks for the gift of life. Edged with silver, soft clouds sailed past the moon. It was hard to go below to sleep.

Reaching north toward Fortune Island the next day, I saw the first yacht I'd seen since Ponce in Puerto Rico, the first yacht underway since leaving the Virgin Islands. She stood out from Fortune Island into the Crooked Island Passage. For a while I followed her, thinking to anchor in Little Harbor on Long Island, but a squall building up to the eastward crippled the wind, making it unlikely that I'd cross the Passage and get the anchor down by dark. In the Bahamas a prudent skipper does not approach unfamiliar islands without sufficient sunlight to whiten the water over shoals and turn it purple over coral heads, so I turned back and tacked for an anchorage off Landrail Point on Crooked Island. Approaching a village south of the point as the squall came over with gusts of wind and rain, I saw a rock out of water ahead. From the rock a long brown underwater streak paralleled the shore. Like most reefs in the clear water of the Bahamas, this one presents little danger in good daylight. At night or in a squall it might easily hole a good ship's bottom.

While I was studying the reef a native boy sculled out from the village. He came aboard and piloted me to an anchorage north of the reef, an anchorage that seemed a good one when we reached it. An hour later, perhaps because the squall had passed or the tide had turned, a wicked surge was curling around Bird Rock to the north, making the ship roll and pitch even after I'd put out a stern anchor.

Choosing an anchorage in the Bahamas requires more thought than a New Englander is likely at first to give. As a rule, in the landlocked harbors of New England, when your anchor is down you can forget about the weather and the wind. Not so in the Bahamas. In the remoter islands at least, you often anchor in what is only a lee, vulnerable to surges in some slants of the Trade and untenable if the wind gets in the north.

Next day, a whole sail breeze astern drove *Little Dipper* across the Crooked Island Passage and up Long Island to Clarence Town, some forty-odd miles, by early afternoon. Rounding Strachan Cay at the mile-wide entrance to Clarence Harbor, I neglected to check bearings on the chart and sailed out of the channel. Alarmed as purple splotches denoting coral heads appeared in the clear water, I hove to to get my bearings. Immediately, as at Crooked Island, a native boy sculled out and volunteered to pilot me. Even when not needed, these pilots are good to have aboard. They are sources of local information and they know sail.

In Clarence Town the Commissioner reversed the procedure I'd grown used to in the Antilles: he gave *me* a cigarette. He also drove me in his car to a grocery store, a tiny one at the edge of town. Like most stores in the remoter islands, this one offered only a few cans of beans, some soft drinks, a bit of candy. I would have enjoyed a change from my diet of corned beef and fish, but as I walked the village's sandy paths and remarked the dignity of the women who nodded to me from the doorways of tiny thatch-roofed huts, as I gammed with men and boys at the mailboat landing, I wondered if it was not to the interest of anyone with tastes like mine that as much of the world as possible remain in British hands. Perhaps because they possess the mental ballast of a tradition which is at bottom religious, Britishers—be they white or yellow or, like the Bahama Commissioners I'd been meeting, black—do not seem as anxious as Americans to make the world over in the name of Progress and the image of Levittown. I'm more than willing to forego the convenience of a supermarket in Clarence Town to have the chance of cruising among islands that still remain much as the Lord saw fit to make them.

I took my departure from Clarence Town on a brilliant sunny morning. A fresh Trade piled up beam seas that sometimes lapped the rail, and *Little Dipper* reached fast and gloriously along the bold Long Island shore. For hours coral cliffs came up over the horizon off the port bow, slid past abeam shining white in the morning sun, and fell away astern while more cliffs came up ahead. Under main and staysail we averaged better than seven knots and were around Cape Santa Maria at Long Island's northern end by 1300. An anchorage which looks snug on the chart can be found under the Cape, but, chancing a night hove to in Exuma Sound if the wind should lighten, I layed a course for George Town.

The Trade was now astern, but a wung-out staysail helped us sight the monument on Stocking Island by mid-afternoon. The wind held, and we were across the harbor bar and tacking up the harbor's green choppy length as the sun was setting. With the staysail furled and the lead going, for yellow patches of shoal water seemed all around, the beat up the harbor toward the lee side of Stocking Island proved a slow one. Before we reached the cove on Stocking Island which I'd hoped to make, dusk dulled the colors of the bottom. I put down the anchor off a white beach under the monument, and the ship lay quiet in still water.

Next morning I rowed across the harbor—it was like rowing across a liquid emerald—to have a look at George Town. The houses were bigger than those in Clarence Town, and George Town boasted several hundred yards of tree-shaded road. But George Town, too, was only a village. A short walk explored it, and I became increasingly aware that by choosing the Bahama route to Florida I had changed the nature of my trip.

Half the interest of an Antillean cruise lies in the towns you visit, in the foreignness of the people and their ways. Ba-

hamians, too, are foreign to Americans, but with the exception
of New Providence their islands are sparsely populated and their
modest villages lack the stir and color of towns and cities further south.

The lure of the Bahamas is pre-eminently to the sailor, and
he may well prefer them to the Antilles, for the geography of
the Antilles from Cuba to the Virgin Islands forces you to sail
either with the Trade or slamming into it. The more widely
scattered Bahamas allow you to play the Trade's slants and so
make wide circles "there and back" without too much windward thrashing. In the deep passages and sounds separating the
remoter Bahamas you get real deep sea sailing—day after day on
long, blue, white-crested seas rolling westward before the Trade
—and you can spend your nights at anchor, untroubled by officials and red tape, off beaches visited only by occasional conch-
collecting natives. Cruising the remoter Bahamas, there is little
to distract you from the fascination of sailing your ship, from
the primordial lure of sea and wind, sky and lonely island.

The Bahamas offer a more varied test of piloting. Antillean
landfalls are mountain tops, but a Bahama landfall is likely to
be only the thin vertical line of a light tower suddenly visible
on an empty sea, or on the same empty sea a clump of brush or
the fronds of palm trees blowing in the wind—and to see them
at all you must be close upon them. The water off Bahama islands is often shoal. Tidal currents wash across these shoals.
Charts are sometimes inaccurate. All this can be made to sound
formidable, but you soon learn to use your brains and eye. And
then, instead of blindly trusting charts and buoys, you come to
enjoy your quickened perception of the colors of the water, of
the rise and fall of the tides, and of the contours of reefs and
coves.

And the Bahamas offer not only ocean sailing but the unique
experience of sailing for miles on shallow banks. In George
Town, I met Linton Rigg and from him got the welcome assur-

ance that there'd be no difficulty in taking *Little Dipper*'s six feet of draft through Galliot Cut and northward inside The Exumas to Nassau.

On the run from George Town north to Galliot Cut the ocean—that's the name for the lower end of Exuma Sound—gave us the fondest of farewells. The Trade blew off the quarter, fresh enough to keep the masthead jib bellied out beyond the headstay. With the boom guyed out and steady, *Little Dipper* went swinging through the seas in such an easy rhythm that it was hard to believe the log, which showed that she was romping along at better than seven knots.

After the mileage on the log sent us close inshore to look for Galliot Cut among the hilly cays sliding past to port, it took time and some manoeuvering along the breakers to locate the light that identifies the Cut. The light turned out to be an electric lantern on a post.

I took in the jib for the sake of manoeuverability and broad-reached for the Cut. Inside it, a commanding wind made light of an adverse current, and after we had furrowed through a few steep swells the ship ran steady as a train. With startling suddenness we left behind us the swing and surge of deep sea sailing, the ocean's cool wind and white-topped indigo seas, and entered waters altogether different. As the Cut's high shores dropped astern, white beaches shimmered in hot sunlight on either hand. Ahead, in warmer air and under a softer breeze, the sands of the Bank spread out enormously, thinly covered by a sheet of bright green water, water only rippled all the way to a glittering horizon.

Galliot Cut invited a lay-over of a day or two. With the ocean just beyond the high tops of the cays, and the green bank stretching away to the westward, the beaches of the Cut looked like perfect places to swim and loaf and sketch, to get the feel of the Exumas. Unhappily my time was running short.

To simplify the piloting I stood out three miles to the deepest water on the Bank before hardening up to reach north for Harvey Cay. By late afternoon the anchor was down in a cove off the northwest end of Harvey Cay—an anchorage which can also be made by night, for the cay has a light and plenty of water all around. Toward dark, clouds thickened to the north and formed a squall line facing south, but unlike the squalls that had preceded a Norther off Hispaniola, this squall drifted westward with the Trade. By dark it had vanished and the sky was bright with stars.

That evening, while the ever-hurrying Trade strummed in the rigging topside, the Nassau radio's broadcasts to the out islands brought a vivid sense of the distances between Bahama islands and of the life Bahamians live:

"By way of a telegram to Henry Rolle on Great Exuma—meet me at George Town in a week and bring a tiller—John Rolle." "By way of a telegram to James Smith on Cat Island—your wife gave birth to a seven pound boy at two PM." "Great Guana Cay—arriving tomorrow for confirmations—Canon Collingwood."

Maintaining a three miles offing the next morning as we continued north along the Exumas, I could not identify the succession of cays hull-down to starboard until Saddle Cay's pronounced saddle between two hills appeared. Getting a fix from this, I rounded the coral heads to the west of Highburn Cay with confidence. Beyond, with the sun high and at my back, I found plenty of water and saw no heads on the short beat eastward to a cluster of uninhabited coral ledges called the Allen Cays.

Thanks to Rigg's BAHAMA ISLANDS and Etheridge's GUIDE TO THE BAHAMAS the entrance into the Allen Cays was quickly spotted. *Little Dipper* went boiling in hard on the wind and riding a current that poured seaward through them. In the fresh breeze we had no difficulty bearing off out of the current and coming to anchor near a big Nassau charter schooner.

Here was one of the snuggest anchorages in the Bahamas and one of the prettiest. Low, sandy, covered with palmettos, the Allen Cays resounded to the crash of combers on their seaward side, while their inner beaches encircled the anchorage, a quiet pond. This pond's water was so clear that only the ripples on its surface betrayed its presence over the sandy bottom. Conch shells lay half buried in the white sand of the beaches. Etheridge's book said that iguanas prowled the brush.

The following morning the schooner we had anchored near went out under power before us, and my little windjammer had the satisfaction of passing her outside as she was hoisting sail and getting ready to stop the engine's racket.

The chart makes the coral heads on the Yellow Bank, astride the course from the Allen Cays to New Providence and Nassau, look dangerous, but most—maybe all—of these heads have ten feet of water over them. With the sun high they are easy to avoid and offer anyone on the thirty mile stretch between the Exumas and New Providence a chance to check his position. As *Little Dipper* ran across this bank before the usual strong Trade, log and lead found the shoalest water where the chart said it should be.

The pine trees of New Providence came up over the horizon off the starboard bow, indicating a strong set to the westward. I hardened up to keep well to the east of East Point and planned to approach Nassau via Porgee Rocks, which on the chart looked prominent. But when dead reckoning indicated we were in position to head for Porgee Rocks on a bearing that would by-pass all charted dangers, Porgee Rocks could not be seen. At first, the distant knolls of New Providence offered no useful bearings. Rose Island to the north was only a line of brush and trees without identifiable feature.

Rigg says that the coral heads shown on the chart in the eastern approaches to Nassau have been dynamited out, but I wondered if the engineers might have overlooked one head, with

*Little Dipper*'s name on it. At length I figured out the chart
location of a large pink hotel, conspicuous several miles to the
east in the direction of the city. When this building bore WxN
I jibed around and headed for it. Following that course, we
came suddenly on Porgee Rocks, low rocks with a pygmy light
on them. From there we had no trouble running down the harbor and rounding up at the floats of the Nassau Yacht Haven.

To my way of thinking Nassau Harbor, as a harbor, must be
one of the worst in the world. Once you have your bearings, it
is easy enough to enter from the east, but to leave or enter its
western end you must cross a bar where there is always a nasty
swell and sometimes a dangerous one. Inside, the greater part
of the harbor is only a hundred yards wide, if that. Always
crowded, the harbor is a thoroughfare between Hog Island and
the quays of Nassau. Tidal currents race through it at three and
even four knots. The Trade blows straight down it, raising a
chop.

But probably no harbor in the world offers more to interest
and delight a sailor. Aside from visiting yachts, big and little,
sail and power, an endless parade of native sloops and schooners
comes in from the out islands with fish and pigs and garden
truck and passengers, and returns whence it came with canned
goods, fuel gas, lumber, and more passengers. There is always
someone making sail, someone anchoring, someone docking or
careening a vessel or trying to stem a tide, on that windy stretch
of emerald water. A sailor can lie in Nassau for a month and
never know a moment's boredom.

From Nassau to Florida I planned the kind of varied route
the Bahamas offer: thirty miles of ocean sailing to the Berry
Islands; along the Berry Island Bank to Northwest Channel
light; sixty-five miles across the Grand Bahama Bank to Gun
Cay and Bimini; then across the Gulf Stream to Palm Beach.

*Little Dipper* crossed the Nassau bar closehauled and so had
no trouble with the swell. From the bar to the Berry Islands

*Bahama News Bureau*

Northwest Channel Light

she had her sheets well started and ran off fast before seas that piled up seven or eight feet high behind her transom. Closing the Berry Islands, I got my bearings from Whale Cay's high white cliffs and by early afternoon lay at anchor under the western end of Bird Cay. That anchorage proved windy and choppy, but I didn't want to lengthen the next day's run by working up into the quieter water off Frazer's Hog Cay. I turned in early, hoping for wind in the morning. We had some eighty miles to sail to the nearest anchorage along our route, at Gun Cay.

We got the wind. By 0930 we had rounded Northwest Channel Light, its skeleton tower seeming from a distance to stand in the open sea marking nothing. In the Bank's green water with a lively breeze astern, I laid a course for Sylvia Bell, forty-seven miles to the west, and hoped that when we'd logged that distance the bell would be in sight. From the bell, the chart showed a course to Gun Cay with a minimum depth of seven feet.

In Nassau I'd been told to allow half a point for the current on the Bank. Although a stranger cannot predict the direction of the set, on any bank he can easily find it out: by slowing his boat or stopping her and leaning over the rail and opening his eyes beneath the surface (or using a water glass). That will show him which way the grass and ferns on the bottom are streaming. But as Northwest Channel Light fell astern, back sights on it revealed no set, and I made no allowance for one. Toward noon a cabin cruiser going east passed close aboard. Taking this as evidence that we were on course, I continued to allow nothing for a set and did not trouble to stop the boat and check. With the sun bright overhead and the breeze dead aft, *Little Dipper* was ticking off six miles or better every hour. She had a long way to go and it seemed a shame to stop her . . .

In late afternoon, when the log put us only five miles short of Sylvia Bell, I was encouraged to see an auxiliary, under power and pitching violently in the Bank's short chop, going east. Figuring she must recently have taken her departure from the bell, I altered course to get on her track and continued on.

As the log spun out the mileage, I unlimbered my binoculars to find the bell—and couldn't find it.

*Little Dipper* ran another mile or two over a clearly visible sand bottom. Still no bell.

Suddenly anything was possible. Maybe the boats I'd sighted had been following courses across the Bank that I didn't know about. If so, sighting those boats had meant nothing. The current I hadn't checked might by now have set me many miles off course, and there was no telling in what direction.

Dropped into the transparent water, the lead found nine feet of depth—just three feet between the bottom and my keel.

I spread out the chart in the cockpit and saw that my sounding suggested we were north of the bell, for the depths south of it tended to be a fathom more. On the other hand, how much trust could be put in soundings on a sandy bottom whose greatest depth was only three fathoms?

According to the chart, the whole western edge of the Bank was shoal and the only way to get off it was to follow the course shown from Sylvia Bell to Gun Cay. We could, however, whether we were north of the bell or south of it, carry our six foot draft for some eight miles further before grounding in the sand bores along the western edge. Hauling in the main to slow her down, I let *Little Dipper* run eight miles.

Still no bell. Now the sun was starting to set, and from horizon to horizon there was nothing at all in sight except the Bank's green water.

I hove to. Using the binoculars, I rubbed my eye along the horizon to the west. Miles away on an otherwise empty sea, I saw the tops of palm trees.

Land all right, but what land? And what depth of water under the choppy green seas now darkening between us and those enigmatic palms? They might be on any cay between Riding Rocks and Bimini.

The sun touched the horizon and the bank looked very lonely. If I were miles off my course and put my ship aground, it might be weeks—or forever—before anyone came by. All I could do was stay hove to and hope that at dark I'd see either the light on the bell or Gun Cay Light. If neither appeared, I'd have to moor the ship and reconnoiter with the dinghy.

I made tea and for some thirty minutes lay hove to, waiting for darkness. Staysail pulled a-weather and mainsail slowly flapping, *Little Dipper* held a steady heel in the splashing chop.

An orange sunset faded. Darkness climbed the eastern sky. And then, as the light drained away and darkness overspread the Bank, a light flashed in the distance. The flash recurred, and I checked its timing. My difficulties were over. Gun Cay Light was on the job and we were not far off the course to it shown on the chart. Soon the ship was on the proper bearing and running it down in a breeze that continued fresh. I never saw the bell.

The light's flashes grew bigger and brighter. Finally the dark bulk of the lighthouse appeared under the flashes, and the sound of surf came up the wind. Shortly we were in the anchorage off Gun Cay's eastern shore.

Rounding up, the ship pitched so heavily in the chop that I decided to hunt smoother water on the cay's Gulf Stream side. From Cat Cay an unmarked reef made out toward the light, and with the fresh breeze driving us fast through the darkness under the light we hugged the rocky shore of Gun Cay so close as to be almost in its surf. We threaded the passage without mishap, jibed over, and found a quiet anchorage in Gun Cay's lee.

The following afternoon we sailed north to Bimini with the Gulf Stream's blue water bordered on the starboard hand by a line of tiny cays and isolated palms and by the green shimmer of the Bank.

At Bimini I anchored off and rowed ashore to get my clearance for the States. Rigg's BAHAMA ISLANDS paints a forbidding picture of the officials I'd be dealing with at Palm Beach, and the Bahamian who sold me my clearance did the same:

"Sport fishermen went across to Palm Beach with a party a few days ago, and the skipper forgot his clearance. They refused to let his passengers land, even though most of them were seasick and *their* papers were OK. They all had to come back here, get cleared, and cross again."

As I listened, doubts about *Little Dipper's* legal status assailed me. That evening I spent some time rigging a sheet across the forward half of the cabin and lettering it "Crew Quarters" to prevent some red tapeworm from measuring her cargo capacity and deciding she required papers I didn't have. (If that happened, said worm would be the first who ever claimed her cabin was too big.

The short reach to Bimini had been made in the first light air I'd encountered in the Bahamas, and now, on the island's western edge, the Bahama wind seemed to have quit for good. Morning came off dead calm. With over eighty miles to go across the Stream to Palm Beach, I decided to lay over. The next morning, too, was calm. Trusting that eventually we'd get wind enough to cross the Stream before it set us north of our objective, I got up the anchor and put the ship on a westward heading.

All morning and all afternoon the only air that stirred came in a series of catspaws, dark blue on the surface and acres in size, moving slowly out of the southwest and whispering across a sea like a silver mirror. As a catspaw reached the ship, she raised a rustle at her stem and bubbles flowed aft along her hull. Then the catspaw passed, and only the lazy slat of a sail or the rattle of a slide broke the stillness under the deep blue sky. In the catspaws we made two knots, between them nothing.

Checking the course we were making, I watched Bimini's profile slowly recede and slowly sink into the glassy water astern. Some time later, the masts of steamers going north in the axis of the Stream appeared ahead. As the hours passed, these successive masts grew higher until superstructures, too, were visible, and finally decks. That hot calm day, with the ship never more than ghosting, furnished graphic proof that the earth on which we sailed was round. No matter what school teachers tell our children, Columbus could not have been the only seaman of his time who knew the earth was round. Anyone who ever watched a point of departure sink below the horizon and a landfall come up over it must have guessed the truth.

Toward evening a southeasterly breeze came in and the ship's hourly strides across the chart began to lengthen. I had planned to get my bearings by the light at Hillsboro Inlet as we closed the American coast, but when that coast rose above a darkened sea the impracticability of the plan was obvious. The coast—soon the entire horizon from north to south—blazed with lights: lights on the shore and back of it, lights low down and lights high up, lights of every color. Hillsboro Light was no doubt one of the glittering many, but in the general glare impossible to identify.

As my little ship rolled through the darkness at six knots, the mighty glare ahead served notice that we had left behind us the kind of world where man, like starfish, stars, and islands, forms part and only part of the scheme of things. That frantically lighted coast proclaimed a world where man, wrapping himself ever tighter in a net of man-made contrivances, was trying to make himself the only thing. Now only astern, above the Bahama Islands, did stars reveal the night sky's depth. Ahead, above that proudly blazing coast, the sky was shallow, lurid with the reflections of artificial lights.

The airplane beacon at Palm Beach proved the only identifiable feature along that coast. Steering by its green and white flashes, I closed the coast and ran north. We were off the Palm Beach breakwaters about an hour before the current tables promised "Flood ends, ebb begins." Wary of the current between the breakwaters, I stood off and on for half an hour, waiting for slack water.

With sheets well started and the breeze still fresh from the southeast, we started through. Halfway in, our reaching breeze changed to a light air from dead ahead. We had some anxious moments tacking up the channel as the ebb began, but before being ignominiously vomited out to sea we managed to slip around the corner into Lake Worth. At 0330, with sails still hoisted and the ship stationary over the bottom but stemming a strengthening current, I made up the anchor and put it down.

Next morning, the Palm Beach officials were friendliness itself. They object to small craft anchoring in the turning basin off the quays. Anchor off the Palm Beach shore and you'll have no trouble.

From St. Thomas in the Virgin Islands *Little Dipper* had coasted for a thousand miles. In all that distance she had had only two days of head winds and spent only four nights at sea. Although sailing without an engine, I had been able to count on making sixty miles between breakfast and supper. On many days I had made much more. The ship had taken not one scratch or bump on her smooth red bottom. She'd had no failures of gear, no torn sails. Warned everywhere along the route that the people a few horizons on would steal my boat or cut my throat, I had met only friendliness.

These days, when headed by the wind along the New England coast and forced to slug to windward for every mile made good, I remember reaching off week after week before a quartering Trade, with flying fish scattering out ahead and blue ocean swells crowding up behind a swinging counter. When the coasts of home grow bleak with winter, the white beaches of Galliot Cut come vividly to mind, and the green Bank spreading westward under a soft blue sky. Cape Samana towers up once more, in memory, and I think of standing on that great cliff's heights and listening to the Trade Wind's music and watching the Trade comb the deep Atlantic. Some evening, too, I'd like to round up inside Hogsty Reef, put down an anchor, and lie there overnight, sheltered from Atlantic rollers by tiny cays and coral heads visited only by infrequent native coasters.

# CHAPTER V

## *Down to Maine—and Back*

From Connecticut I've cruised to Maine five times. I've never sought nor found what a little ship does not always find, and I've never dulled the joy of finding it. When *Little Dipper* has threaded Watch Hill Passage and started sheets to a good sou'-wester, shore ties and shore ambitions drown in her bubbling wake and every swing of her counter brings me closer to those First Things that make all other things worth having. The dunes of the coast, the sea, the look of the sky, the heat of the sun and the coolness under the stars, working a little ship, a meal and a sleep—these become all that matter. Senses sharpen, bone and muscle come alive, and familiar hills and headlands come over the horizon fresh and new. Soon Maine's blue days and well known islands beckon in imagination as, to sailors when the world was young, Hi Brasil once did.

*Little Dipper*'s lack of engine makes distance, calm, and slant of wind imposing, rest and harbor sometimes questionable, and so helps cruising weave its welcome spell. Or does that spell—and *Little Dipper*'s lack of engine—evidence mere childishness? I leave you to your own opinion. As the Doc opined while *Little Dipper* lay motionless in a two day calm off Nova Scotia, "Most of the trouble in this world gets started by altruists. I look out for Number One."

The spell was working in '57 when *Little Dipper*, once more bound "down to the east'ard," slipped out of Block Island's Salt Pond and ghosted north at dawn along that island's sandy shore. Morning haze lay on the sea, and ground fog brimmed the hollows among the island's hills and flowed in billows to the beach. But the tops of the hills stood up clear and green, and over the top of one green hill a big red sun had thrown his upper limb.

My ship had steerage way, no more. Her hull slid through the water without a sound. Overhead a gull flew north along our course, his underbody crimsoned by the rising sun, his wings' slow beat not disturbing the perfection of the silence. Ghosting through the hush and pure air of that sunrise was like ghosting through the first sunrise that ever lighted up this earth.

By eight o'clock auxiliaries under power were passing us. By ten we had a breeze. Running for Buzzards Lightship that afternoon before a sou'wester smoking across a rising sea, we overtook the boat that had passed us last. As we drew abeam of her the slatting of her jib club sounded clearly across the hiss and splash of intervening seas. "Bam!" went the club to port, then "Bam!" to starboard, making *Little Dipper*'s equally lazy but loosefooted headsails a source of satisfaction.

Why, I wondered, did so many skippers club their headsails? A club clutters up the foredeck, spoils the set of the sail, and cannot readily be hauled a-weather for heaving to to rest or tend the stove. You say a clubbed headsail lets you tack without tending sheets? Trim a loosefooted headsail amidships. You'll sail about as fast and be equally able to tack without tending sheets.

At 1330 Buzzards Lightship came out of a thickening haze ahead. Just as well it did come, too, because only when close to its high red hull could I hear its horn's familiar organ tone. Under its stern I hardened sheets and with the ship well heeled and crashing proudly through smoky whitecaps shaped a course for Vineyard Sound. To port, the backs of breakers on the Sow and Pigs wheeled past. Ahead, the cliffs of Cuttyhunk, then those of Nashawena, stood up dim and ghostly, wreathed in golden haze. They dropped astern like frontiers of a just

Cornet

Little Dipper

glimpsed land of dream. Off Tarpaulin Cove I doused headsails, readied the anchor, and worked inshore with mainsail
luffing and the lead swinging.

A few days earlier luck had arranged a meeting with Berno
and Hima (Forbes) Gerault, en route to spend the summer in
the solitary house, once postoffice for schooners in the coasting
trade, at Tarpaulin Cove. Ashore that evening the Geraults
gave me the freedom of Naushon. Next day I hiked its beech
woods and stalked its deer on bayberry moors above the sea.

Clan Forbes, who have owned Naushon, Pasque, and Nashawena Islands for generations, would open more of this romantic
empire to the public, had the public not proved itself untrust-
worthy. Not only are there frequent attempts to poach deer,
but several times each summer a bell at Hadley Harbor tolls,
calling the clan to fight fires which picnickers have started and
failed even to report. Down timber from storms makes the
fire danger especially acute.

"Here's hoping you never open up these islands," I told my
hosts. "As they are, they're enjoyed by everyone cruising past.
Keeping them unspoiled is a public service." Not married then,
I added, "But how I'd like a foothold on them! Maybe I'll put
on my best clothes, go to Boston, and try to marry a Forbes."

Hima, Berno, and their children chorused, "If you want to
impress a Forbes, wear your *worst* clothes!"

The Elizabeth Islands are in good hands.

Although the Army Engineers forbid it, certain windjamming people have sailed through the Cape Cod Canal. It's said
that when a patrol boat ordered one of these reactionaries to
turn on a non-existent engine, he sent a crew member below
to bang a frypan against the stove and blow pipe smoke out of
the scuttle, indicating an engine trying hard to keep within the
law—whereat the patrol boat, duped, sheered off. To me of
course this is only hearsay. From Naushon my windjammer was
bound for Hyannis and thence around Monomoy and the Cape.

We reached Hyannis in a hard norther under staysail and reefed main, and the statement that I'd reefed while under way occasioned some surprise ashore. In truth, reefing *Little Dipper* strains a singlehander not at all, and the same must hold for any well rigged ship. When it gusted up that afternoon and *Little Dipper* began dragging her turnbuckles through a nasty foam-streaked chop, the problem wasn't reefing but, while reefing, keeping bearings and avoiding being set onto shoals by Nantucket Sound's strong current. The problem was solved by closing on a buoy off Menauhant and heaving to under backed staysail and partly lowered main. A little trimming of the staysail and the rudder kept the vessel stemming the current, and she lay quietly near the buoy while I tied in the reef. Knowing you can solve such problems would seem essential to happy singlehanding.

While lying in Hyannis I re-read, for the good of my soul, the CRUISING GUIDE's account of the well-skippered yawl which went aground in fog off Monomoy and became a total loss. Monomoy and Pollock Rip demand respect. So does Cape Cod's harborless outer coast.

A nice land breeze wafted us past Point Gammon on a bright blue morning and set me hoping for an early arrival at the bell off Handkerchief Shoal. But the land breeze died. We didn't reach the bell till 1500 of a hazy afternoon, and by then were closehauled to a breeze from the foggy quarter, southeast. Not intending to tack past Monomoy in fog, I anticipated anchoring south of the channel, but the breeze strangely brought no fog. Monomoy slid safely past, a distant stripe of sand between gray sea and sullen sky.

We cleared the Slue on the first of the flood, which flows seaward here, and took a departure northward under a clearing sky. Miles of pot buoys, by far the largest concentration of them I'd ever seen, were streaming northward in the current. Bear-

ings and the log showed that this current added a knot and a
half to the speed we got from a following breeze.

As the dunes of the Cape turned blue with evening the
breeze lightened and I gave less attention to the ship than to
sea and sky and lonely twilit coast. In the day's last light I
leafed through Henry Beston's OUTERMOST HOUSE, chronicle
of a "year of life on the Great Beach of Cape Cod," and off
Eastham Bar toasted him in good New England rum. The sun
went down in a violet haze and the breeze all but died, but
lights shining here and there across the smooth black water advised that draggers were about. It seemed wise to stay on deck
until the last of them had disappeared. Then I lowered the main
to the gallows, hung a lantern in the shrouds, and went below
and slept.

We lay becalmed all morning, but at noon a southerly got up.
It gave us an easy run to Peaked Hill Bar and freshened as we
began the lengthy process of rounding the Cape to enter Provincetown. For *Little Dipper* that afternoon it was reach, beat,
and a tack to clear Wood End, a reach to Long Point, and a
final run to the anchorage off the steamer dock. Maneuvering
around this anchorage in a fresh breeze and a rising chop, finding nowhere to escape the chop and remarking the harbor's
yawning openness to the east, brought to mind a verse inscribed
by Hilaire Belloc in a guest book forced on him by an eager
innkeeper:

> "I made my passage through St. Alban's Race
> And came to anchor in this bloody place."

Ashore, the skipper of the handsome party schooner *Hindu*
told me that while Long Point offered something of a lee in an
easterly, the bottom there fell off so steeply that an anchor
would not hold. About all you can do in Provincetown in an
easterly blow is bury an anchor out of water on Long Point's

beach and put another anchor astern in case the wind backs. Or put to sea.

From Provincetown a fine sou'wester blew us smartly across Massachusetts Bay and into yacht-filled Marblehead, where I had a day to kill before the Doc and his Jean could join me for the run to Rockport on Cape Ann.

"Why don't you call on Mr. Herreshoff?" Selman Graves of the Graves Shipyard suggested. "He's a fine old gentleman and the Castle's just up the hill from here."

Plenty of fine old gentlemen don't welcome calls from strangers, but I worked up the hill to the Castle's turrets and battlemented walls and passed boldly through an iron gate that bore the wrought iron letters "L. Francis Herreshoff—Yachts."

Thin, tall, blue-eyed, with a bright red Kaiser Wilhelm moustache, Mr. Herreshoff answered my knock. After instructing a brace of poodles that I must not be eaten, he cordially asked me in. Looking out a window of the Castle's baronial hall at *Little Dipper* riding to her anchor in the harbor, he murmured words I well remember: "Any boat designed by Starling Burgess is artistic." Seaworthy, fast, able, in Herreshoff's league you take all that for granted. You ask, "Has she character? Is she beautiful?"

During the two hour gam that followed I steered the talk to Joshua Slocum, with whom and on whose *Spray* my host had sailed in boyhood. In his opinion Slocum and *Spray* had been prime examples of the saying "It ain't the ships but the men in 'em." Slocum, my host declared, had got unwieldy *Spray* around the world by virtue of consummate seamanship. She'd been poorly found and none too strongly rigged, but aboard of her there'd been something better than stainless steel and depth of pocketbook—a "superhuman" faculty for judging just what strains worn rope and metal could endure.

Another thing: Joshua Slocum was the most deliberate sailorman who ever hoisted sail. Not for Slocum the acrobatic leaps and flashing hands of weekend athletes. Slocum relied on know-how and took it easy. Shooting for a dock, he left his helm long before you'd dare leave yours and strolled forward at a pace that brought him to *Spray*'s bow at just the moment when that bow was six feet off the dock.

My host rose from his chair, called a nearby stack of books a bollard, and went through what seemed the motions of a work-man slowly measuring the bollard for a collar. It was Joshua Slocum taking a round turn with his dock line.

On second thought, Slocum's deliberation hadn't been unique. Jim Davidson, master carpenter and rigger in the Her-reshoff yard at Bristol—with a broad axe he could cut a chip "big enough to cook your breakfast" along the chalk line of a solid spar—had also been a man to take his time. Working aloft in a bo'sun chair on a J boat long ago, Jim Davidson had for half an hour heard queries hollered at him from the deck by an owner anxious to get under way: "How're you coming along up there?" and "How soon'll you be done?" A hundred and thirty feet above the deck, Jim didn't answer, but finally signaled to be lowered. On deck he faced the eager owner. "Mister," Jim said, "if you know someone can do this job faster'n me, you go ahead and hire him." And then, with an agonized owner watch-ing, Jim Davidson ambled back to his bo'sun chair, slowly worked back into it, and was slowly hoisted a hundred and thirty feet back to the still unfinished job.

As he had in print, Mr. Herreshoff criticized the ocean racing handicap rule for encouraging undue beam. He pointed out that beaminess increases costs without increasing length, the dimension that makes for ability and speed. I thought he had a point, for it often seems that to get good ratings designers pack as much expensiveness as possible into a given length rather than trying to stretch a given sum of money into the greatest length consistent with seaworthiness.

The following morning I rowed ashore to meet the Doc for

the first time since a yarn about a cruise we'd made to Nova
Scotia had appeared in print. As a connoisseur of literature, he
stated, he approved the yarn, but as a devotee of truth felt
strongly that it failed to bring out the full horror of windjamming in a down east fog. Fastening his gaze on a small boy
standing near, he boomed aloud:

> "*I* could a tale unfold whose lightest word
> Would harrow up thy soul, freeze thy young blood,
> Make thy knotted and combined locks to part
> And each particular hair to stand on end
> Like quills upon the fretful porpentine—"

"Anyway," I said, "it's good to see you, Porcupine."

"Porpentine," he said. "And don't forget I have a lame back."

We were under way by ten o'clock of a clear blue morning.
A fair breeze on a smooth sea brought us around the twin towers
of Thacher's Island and into stone-quayed Rockport by early
afternoon.

Andy Lindsay, with us on our cruise to Novy, and later
aboard *Little Dipper* to the Virgin Islands, was teaching seamanship at the Manchester Yacht Club not far away. Earlier
that year he'd been the only American sailor aboard *Mayflower
II* on her trip from England. His reply that evening to my question about the crossing was succinct: "boring." Even in Alan
Villiers' hands *Mayflower II* could not get out of her own way,
much less to windward. It was pleasant, though, some months
later, to find Andy named in Villiers' account of the crossing
as one of the ship's "two best seamen."

I suggested to the Doc that Jean and he continue on with me
for a few days and a look at Maine.

"No engine," he mused, "and the cruel sea. Maine and the
*foggy* sea! You know, sometimes these days I drive up on these
Cape Ann headlands and gaze out over all that ocean we had to
cross to get to Novy. Memories of that cruise come flooding

back, and I feel fascinated. Fascinated. Like a little bird looking at a great snake!" He sighed. "And this time you want Jean to come too. It reminds me of a remark that almost lost me a couple of patients a few days ago."

I waited.

The Doc said, "I happen to be one of the few doctors left who'll make house calls. It's because I'm a conservative and not a do-gooder. Anyway, one evening I called on a lady patient who had another lady visiting her. This second one also had something wrong, and my patient introduced us and asked if I'd check her friend over too. So without really thinking, just to say it gracefully or something, I said sure—I'd kill two birds with one stone. Oh, my-oh-my!"

"Remind me to get your help next time I have to say something graceful," I said.

"All right, I will. But you and your boat don't get to make an orphan out of our Johnny."

He refused to budge from "home and duty to humanity," and I cruised on alone.

A remark attributed to Bismarck has often prodded me to read further in books on the art of sailing. "Fools," that astute man said, "learn by experience. I learn by the experience of others." But that wisdom can turn around and bite. It did so a few hours after I'd left Rockport.

Seated on a pitching bridge deck, I was watching my ship's bow alternately plunging into a steep chop and leaping skyward, trying to yank her anchor out of the Isles of Shoals' not always reliable mud. Since *Little Dipper* first poked her nose among their channels, the remote and windswept barrenness of these Isles has often drawn me back, often enough for even a fool to learn to put his anchor down where the holding ground is best and some of the sea raised by a nor'west breeze is damped —in toward the riprap joining Star and Cedar Islands. This I'd failed to do and now, in late afternoon, a nor'west breeze was freshening across the unobstructed eight miles of ocean from my bow to the New Hampshire coast. Aboard a windjammer, shifting an anchorage is work. If learning by experience was for fools, the word for me was idiot.

But by 1800 the genial principle that looks out for pregnant women, drunks and idiots made its appearance. The wind began to drop. An hour or so later a red fair weather sun was going down behind a solitary cloud. The sea shone like a mirror all the way to the New Hampshire coast. That night I slept the sleep of the lucky, so often sounder than the sleep of the just.

Morning came off sunny, blue, and cool. To the nor'west Mt. Agamenticus, forerunner of the hills of Maine, stood up clear and blue, its round slopes dappled by the shadows of small clouds. Turning to windward all morning in a light air on a smooth blue sea, it looked like Cape Porpoise would be our harbor for the night, and that brought to mind my first trip from the Shoals to Porpoise, years before.

That time, too, we'd had a beat to Porpoise, but under dark hurrying clouds and smack into burly seas rolled up by a nor'-easter that really whistled. A mean day, that one, fierce and cold and rainy, a rugged initiation to the outer coast both for me and for my son, aged ten. Sixty foot *Baruna* had anchored near us at the Shoals, and, somewhat enviously I'd thought, my son's eyes had measured her mighty length when she weighed anchor before us and moved out. Heeled over and going like a train in weather to her liking, she'd quickly vanished into rain and murk.

Late that afternoon, under staysail and double-reefed main, my son and I came charging into Cape Porpoise's narrow harbor in a howling squall lit by lightning flashes, and found big *Baruna* anchored. As I payed out the rode and we fell back near *Baruna,* her owner appeared in her cockpit and the following exchange occurred:

*Baruna*'s owner to my small drenched son, aged ten: "What time did you leave the Shoals?"

Aged Ten: "About half an hour after you did."

*Baruna*'s Owner: "Must be an able vessel you've got there!"

Aged Ten (with offhand glance at big *Baruna*): "Well, I guess your vessel's pretty able too."

But now the day at hand began to come alive. Inland of the coast cumulus clouds were fountaining up, and the light nor'-easterly air veered and strengthened. An onshore breeze came in. Soon I was laying the course for Portland Lightship and making a nice five knots across a rippled sea. By 1300 whitecaps were flashing in the sun and *Little Dipper* had her shoulder in a curling bow wave and was logging better than six knots. Glorying in conditions almost perfect, her skipper sang and she sped on, both headsails fat and prosperous with reaching wind.

Cape Porpoise moved past two miles to port, its pines and their sawtooth skyline saluted as another forerunner of Maine— for Maine, as is well known, begins at Casco Bay. Soon the white buildings of the Coast Guard station on Wood Island lay abeam, then Wood Island went hull down astern. Now the water between whitecaps was darkly ruffled by the wind, the log was humming in Bahama Islands style, and our wake streamed aft at seven knots. Portland Lightship came over the horizon, and for a while I steered for the tower on Halfway Rock and thought of a visit to the lobster "car" at Mackerel Cove. But the wind held, I hardened sheets, and the ship raced on.

High Seguin rose up ahead, and on its top the lighthouse, white and bright in the light of a westering sun. The wind began to lighten, but as Seguin's brown cliffs and summer-yel-lowed grass came into focus our speed was still six knots. Seguin's high cliffs wheeled past to port against the piney sky-line of the Kennebec shore, and now the sun had dropped below the horizon astern and the bulge of ocean between the sun and us cast a darkening shadow higher and higher into the east-

ern sky ahead. For half an hour a band of rosy light glowed at
the upper edge of that rising shadow. Stars came out, the wind
lightened more, yet there was still a busy rustling at *Little
Dipper*'s bow.

Even on a clear night closing the Maine coast can be tricky,
for dark islands do not readily distinguish themselves from a
dark mainland, but lights and ranges make Boothbay easy. Our
breeze nearly died as we rounded the Cuckolds. At Squirrel Island we were only inching through the darkness. The anchor
wasn't down in Boothbay Harbor until 2300. But after a slow
morning we'd logged more than sixty miles that perfect day.

Of the Coast of Maine, that coastwise cruiser's paradise, I'll
mention only:

Mornings thick o' fog, with the ship lying motionless to a
slackened rode, her decks and rigging soaked with moisture,
fog hiding all but a few feet of gray water . . . and fog brightening and thinning overhead, the sun's warmth coming through,
and a rocky beach and clumps of pines shouldering into view
. . . and, perhaps off Pemaquid, the sun breaking through and
a blue sky deepening and arching cloudless all the way from
pine tree tops to the ocean's distant rim.

And the snap and chill of morning . . . and breakfasts that go
on and on, through bacon, eggs, and muffins to pancakes or
French toast and floods of coffee . . . and lobsters fresh from a
lobsterman's wet glove in harbors anywhere from Casco Bay
to Cutler . . . and the sweetest corn that mortal tooth ever tore
from cob, pulled from stalks that breathe salt air . . . and on
sunny hillsides or in openings in cool woods raspberries, blue-
berries, blackberries, strawberries by the hatful.

And sheltered twisting passages, like the one from Friend-
ship to Port Clyde, between spruce islands unmarked and an-
nually untrod by man . . . the silence of secluded anchorages as
the sun goes down.

And as you reach eastward into Penobscot Bay, the whole range of the Camden Hills rolling northward clear and blue . . . and the noble profile of Isle au Haut . . . the uninhabited islands off Merchant Row, their timber rising thickly from shores of smooth pink granite . . . and, a good day's sail from the wind and surge of open ocean, tranquil Blue Hill Bay set among green pastures and farmers' woodlots . . . and the Western Way, whitecapped by a following breeze, with the heights of Mount Desert towering up above a swinging bowsprit.

And far from least on *Little Dipper*'s cruises down to Maine, old friends welcoming her from familiar docks . . .

In '57 it added up, as it always does, to the conviction that this cruise, this year, had been the best one yet to Maine.

Homeward bound one evening, the ship was gliding southward through smooth water in the last breath of a summer day's sou'wester. Off the quarter a red sun was sinking toward the bluffs of Cape Elizabeth. Astern, the islands of Casco Bay were growing dim, their outlines merging in blue evening haze. As daylight left the sky, that haze turned violet, spread seaward, and ringed the whole horizon.

We'd had a splendid day, the ship sailing to windward at a steady heel, her skipper aware only of the luffs of the sails and of pine-dark islands and headlands moving past beneath a brilliant sky. Now, as the breeze died and haze seemed to shrink the sea, moon and evening star appeared, reminders that the earth we cruised was itself cruising among the stars, all courses set by a Master Navigator. Glad to be aboard, I filled my lungs with cool sea air and sang a loud Doxology.

Before I hove her to that night Boon Island's light had come over the horizon. To the north huge ghostly arms, the northern lights, waved goodbye from hull-down Maine.

Returning from Maine in September, you'll sometimes get a norther that blows you along the coast in sixty mile jumps, longer if you sail at night. But a fresh sou'wester made *Little Dipper* beat for Rockport, and we sailed from Rockport in a sou'wester fresher still. Small craft warnings and hard gusts whirling through the harbor urged a lay-over, but a weather report predicted the arrival of a high. Maybe the strong sou'wester blowing would let me lay the course to Peaked Hill Bar. Maybe it would bring me off Monomoy at just about the time the high came in. And maybe that high would provide a northerly slant for a fast reach through the Slue. So ran my thoughts, and similarly have run the thoughts of countless skippers aiming to get home from Maine.

We raced out of Rockport under staysail and reefed main, came on the wind in big gray rollers sweeping past Thacher's Island, and my hopes fell through. Rail down and spray flying, *Little Dipper* made knots but could not lay the course to Peaked Hill Bar.

Hoping for a lift but never getting one, we slugged it out on the starboard tack through all of a dark and boisterous afternoon. Toward dark, dead reckoning put us seven miles northeast of Peaked Hill Bar and headed further out to sea. I was soaked and tired and ready to settle for Provincetown. I tacked ship, glumly noted that we tacked in ten points, not eight, and above the noise of wind and sea heard the sound of tearing sail cloth forward. Peering toward the sound through failing light, I saw a ragged tear in my hardworking staysail.

When I slacked the mainsheet to ease the motion for a sail change, the main flogged loudly, warning me to damp its flog by easing the halyard. Ignoring the warning, I bent on a storm staysail as fast as darkness and a leaping deck allowed. Returning to the wheel, I got her driving through the seas again. Then, within one minute, Father Neptune meted out stern justice: lights of two steamers coming up astern informed me I was in a steamer lane; fog suddenly streamed through the cockpit; my callousness toward my mainsail paid off in a sound of tearing sail cloth right above my head.

Clawing the soaked canvas off the boom and bending on a smaller dacron main, pumping the foghorn meanwhile, with the ship wallowing in steep seas, left little lungpower for dox-ologies. I didn't eat until we'd put the steamer lane astern and lay slatting in a calm somewhere to the westward of Race Point. At dawn we drifted slowly into Provincetown under storm staysail and small main, and even Provincetown looked good to us. It's doubtful we looked good to Provincetown.

Next morning came off bright, with small craft warnings fly-ing in the town and a strong wind blowing from the west. Such wind seemed to promise a fast reach down the Cape in the smooth water of a lee, and perhaps, I hoped, there'd be a new slant when needed at the Slue. Encouraging this hope, the cur-rent tables advised that the tide would turn to run our way through the Slue at 1955.

Under small main and two headsails we tacked around Race Point, jibed over, and began reaching along the beach. At 1125 the top of the Pilgrim Monument bore west above the crests of yellow dunes. Seaward, the horizon was sharp and clear. No clouds marred the sky's blue depths. At Peaked Hill Bar the sea was smooth in offshore wind, and curlicues of foam raced past the rail at seven knots. Blue sky, smooth sea, fair wind and plenty of it. The skipper sang.

Off Nauset conditions abruptly changed. The continual small hardenings-up required to follow the curving beach had put us hard on the wind, and the flood tide running north along the beach was kicking up a steep sea from dead ahead. In that head sea the ship pitched and plunged. Every time the bow leapt up the jib flogged wickedly. Thankful for my downhaul, I took in the jib, but the wind strengthened until I judged it was blowing thirty knots. It continued blowing from the west, and that and its increasing strength put a different look on the fair tide promised at the Slue. What would the Slue turn into when a two or three knot current began bucking such a wind? Could *Little Dipper* hope to tack through safely in such conditions? Foolishly, I vetoed heaving to offshore, and decided to thread the Slue while the tide still was foul. Wind and current would be against us, but in agreement with each other. Between the lines of buoys as we neared them the sea looked less rough than elsewhere. We might get nowhere, or we might beat through before the tide turned and the seas went crazy.

Judging by a wildly tossing channel buoy, our first two boards yielded about ten yards. The next two gave us twenty. We kept at it, short tacking between the lines of buoys in half a gale as darkness fell. For an hour in whistling wind and pitching cockpit I labored steadily—got her driving, sent her up, slacked one runner, set up the other, cast off the staysail sheet, brought her over, grabbed the lee sheet and belayed it. As the turn of the tide approached, the ship did better with every tack, but we were slugging it out half a mile to leeward of Stone Horse Lightship when the turn did come.

Within ten minutes the seas rearing up ahead against the black night sky were monstrous. Ragged with foam, gleaming darkly, those sharp crests stood *Little Dipper* on her transom, then hove her skyward and seesawed her down. Her bowsprit dove for the bottom, then probed the windy sky. The wind howled, solid water washed across the foredeck, but somehow she kept sailing. For half an hour, short tacking all the time, though now leaving the staysail trimmed amidships on both tacks, I gave thanks for every inch of my ship's draft and forefoot and for the staying granted by her double head rig. Driving, tacking, never hesitating, she gave final proof of her reliability in stays.

I bore off for Nantucket convinced that that thrash through Pollock Rip Channel had been among the severest tests my ship had met. Far from pleased with my judgment in sailing her into such wild water, I gained a deepened respect for Starling Burgess and for the honest Swedes who shaped her timbers and fastened her cedar planks. How much we boat owners owe to the often anonymous men who fit our wood, drill it plumb, and fasten it securely!

From Nantucket we rode a fair tide past Wood's Hole and down to Cuttyhunk in one day. Next day the wind went light, and *Little Dipper* lay that evening in the elbow of the breakwater at Point Jude. A long mile from rows of lights ashore, that elbow made a good last anchorage for a cruise. You seldom feel more free aboard your ship than when she's anchored off the lights and sounds of life ashore.

Some day, I thought on deck that night, crowds may travel to the moon and back, and on both legs of that journey smell no land or sea, feel no wind, know no fatigue, use not one limb or brain cell. That utter insulation from First Things, indeed from all experience whatsoever, will be hailed as Progress. From it, too, some men will welcome a good offing. They can count on finding it sailing down to Maine and back.

# CHAPTER VI

## *A Wife's First Cruise*

By 1958 summer afternoons in Fisher's Island Sound, summer weeks bound to and from the piney thoroughfares of Maine, other weeks running free before blue ocean seas under Caribbean skies, nights at anchor under stars, had sealed me of the Water Rat's philosophy. "There is nothing half so much worth doing," that thinker has laid down, "as messing about in boats."

And then I discovered that in common with philosophers who keep most resolutely dry, the Water Rat had pressed a good case too far. He had overlooked marriage.

In November 1958 I took a bride. She had never been to sea. The following spring she signed on for a summer cruise to Maine.

During May I tried to rid my ship of the marks of bachelorhood and singlehanding. Fid in hand, I scraped and gouged out cabin corners caked with a decade's gurry. I laid linoleum on the cabin sole. Remembering other trips to Maine, I sang the joys of Maine's blue days and blue horizons, Maine's tang of salt and sun-warmed pine. I begrudged no effort to ensure a perfect cruise, and described a great deal of it in advance. At stake, I reasoned privately, was a way of life.

June 1959 came in with rain, and rain fell dismally throughout the month. July blanketed Connecticut in fog. On the day of our departure sea and sky were visible, but gray.

"Fog may close in again," I granted, as *Little Dipper* reached slowly eastward through Watch Hill Passage. "But we've got six weeks—by now the law of averages is on our side!"

Perched on the cockpit coaming, my bride silently gazed off

105

to starboard where, less than a cable length away, sluggish swells were humping up on Catumb Rocks and crashing down in foam. Like everyone else in Stonington she knew that two weeks earlier one of the finest yachts along the coast had struck those rocks in fog and been pounded into total loss.

The gray haze hanging over Block Island Sound's gray swells soon thickened into fog.

Lucy

"Usually," I said, "when you make Block Island you watch the hilltops come up over the horizon. Then you steer for a yellow bluff, and finally you see moors as green as Ireland with small white houses on them."

"It must be pretty," she said, "when you can see it."

We saw little of it that afternoon and less that evening. Morning came off dark.

My hope in the law of averages survived a slow run under sullen skies to Buzzards Lightship, but received a blow when, at the lightship, a bank of fog came up astern on a freshening sou'west breeze. Spreading out a chart in the rolling cockpit as fog streamed through the rigging, I figured a compass course for Cuttyhunk, seven miles to the eastward—and remarked an interesting absence of bells or whistles along that course and at the rocky target.

Allowing half a point for the current pouring over the Sow and Pigs, we hardened up and got on course. The ship heeled and began to drive through rising seas and thickening fog.

"Darling," I said, "you might man the horn—three blasts a minute."

They say a busy crew's a happy one.

A half hour later, with a fresh breeze crooning through the rigging and *Little Dipper* moving fast through beam seas and flying fog, a sudden shadow loomed to port, and a dragger, ploughing through the seas at a good ten knots, plunged across our bow with little more than a coat of paint to spare. Its whistle for the first time audible, the dragger vanished instantly.

My bride's eyes had widened. I felt a tingling at my scalp. Throwing a noisy bow wave, our ship went lunging on through thick gray vapor.

Was half a point, I wondered, enough allowance for the current under us—or too much?

"Maybe," I muttered, watching the compass and straining to pick up sounds of other vessels or of breakers on the Sow and Pigs, "the fog'll be thinner in Cuttyhunk's lee. Anyway, we'll hear surf before we strike."

"Before we strike," my new wife said—and pumped the horn right womanfully.

As the log swinging above the counter warned that we'd

sailed our seven miles, a low rift opened in the fog and revealed a stony beach ahead.

"I know that beach," I said, relaxing.

My bride summed up what had evidently been a revealing study of her husband's face: "You were just as anxious as I was!"

Understatement—and made only seconds before the beach disappeared and the fog around us thickened. Course a little altered to find and thread the channel between Penikese and Cuttyhunk, we sighted a ghostly buoy, sailed past it, and sighted another. In fog thick enough to stand on, my bride received and put into practice a lesson in how to keep a vessel hove to beside a buoy in a current, and I took in the headsails.

Bride steering and skipper heaving the lead, we tacked by the compass toward the entrance to Cuttyhunk's inner harbor. From a final buoy we sailed a compass course until the weedy rocks of a jetty came out of the fog below the bowsprit. Seconds later, as sandy shores materialized off port and starboard rails and we knew we'd made the entrance, an outboard came out the murk astern.

"A yawl just struck at Canapitsit," the outboard's driver called across our rail. Vanishing into the fog ahead, he called back, "She's gone down."

" 'Gone down,' " my bride echoed. She looked at me. "That must mean she—*sank!*"

No other meaning came to mind.

"He must have had an engine," I said, "to go for Canapitsit in a fog like this. Windjamming, he'd have stood off—and still have his bottom under him."

"I'm looking forward to a tot of rum," my bride announced. I heard her murmur, "Quite possibly, several."

By the time we had the anchor down and the rum poured we'd seen the yawl's company brought safe ashore.

"It's like I've told you," I pointed out. "Not having an engine keeps us clear of trouble."

"I'm ready for my next rum," she replied.

When we sailed out next morning the masthead of the sunken yawl slanted forlornly above the gray surface of the Canapitsit channel. We gave it only a glance, for we had a disaster of our own to contemplate: after six years' uncomplaining service the drive shaft of *Little Dipper*'s head had chosen this, the third day of my bride's first cruise, to part. Half of the shaft was still in place. The other half was fast to a useless pump handle now hove into the forepeak.

As *Little Dipper* ambled off before a sluggish breeze with the Elizabeth Islands—golden-cliffed, romantic on sunny days! —looming bleak and dark under yet another soggy sky, I pointed out that we did have paper buckets aboard. Granted that these buckets had to be hoisted topside and hove over, they did fit into the toilet bowl. That was *something*, wasn't it?

My bride said with scrupulous exactitude, "It's not exactly the arrangement I expected."

By the look of the sky the law of averages had been repealed.

At three P.M. we had the anchor down at Vineyard Haven and the head ashore at a shipyard where, I trusted, they could weld the shaft or build a new one.

Next morning, after I'd rowed my bride ashore to buy supplies, the shipyard informed me that it could neither weld the shaft nor build a new one. A new shaft was essential, and to get it someone would have to call New York. I called New York, and discovered that to get a shaft you had to call Baltimore. Baltimore agreed to ship the shaft—which by now seemed the real guts of any cruising operation—to a yard in Boothbay. Then I rowed to a public dock where my bride stood waiting with the groceries.

"Darling," I said, "for six years that head—"

"Yes, dear," she said. "There's a store handy by that sells paper buckets."

A nice sou'wester—triply welcome under the circumstances—wafted us clear of Vineyard Haven and bellied out the main as we bore away for Chatham and Cape Cod. By noon, sunlight was filtering through a summer haze and a chuckle of water at *Little Dipper*'s stem was strengthening into laughter. Rolling easily, the ship began to lift and surge in a familiar rhythm.

"This," I announced, "is more like cruising!"

With the decks drying and a hurrying hull spreading wings of foam across sunny overtaking seas, it surely was more like cruising, and when my bride stretched out along the bridge deck to make acquaintance with Duncan and Blanchard's CRUISING GUIDE I thought the situation well in hand. Who presents the Water Rat philosophy more seductively than Duncan and Blanchard?

"There'll be a difference from now on," my bride said.

"Sunshine and a lively breeze—I hope!"

"I mean that cutting board I got in Vineyard Haven."

"Cutting board?"

"I measured for it—and it fits right over the sink. Now we'll have real salads!"

Contentedly, she began to read.

Minutes later I heard a murmured protest—"Oh—*no!*"—and saw her scowling into the open CRUISING GUIDE.

Eyes fixed on the page, she said aloud, "Whose idea was *this?*"

"What idea?"

"Us going around Monomoy and the Cape—after Chatham. It says here Monomoy may be the most dangerous place on the New England coast!" Eyes still on the page and opening wider, she continued, "It tells about a well found yawl with a practically perfect skipper. They tried to get around Monomoy and —" she stared at me "—they *sank!* Like that boat at Cuttyhunk!"

I recognized what our British cousins call a sticky wicket.

My bride said, "You advised me to read this volume. You said it would enlighten me on what cruising's all about. Have you read it yourself?"

I said I had.

She waved it in the air. "Have you read about this boat that *sank?*"

"That boat didn't really sink," I said. "She just grounded and filled."

"As far as I'm concerned, she *sank*. Trying to go around Monomoy!"

In the ensuing discussion I tried to steer between the Scylla of minimizing danger and the Charybdis of exaggerating it. My peroration included the statement that *Little Dipper* and I had rounded Monomoy more than once, and had not *sunk*.

My bride fell silent, but her knitted brows indicated an earnest effort to unravel a fundamental problem. At length she said, as much to herself as me, "First there was that boat that sank at Watch Hill before we left. Then the boat that sank at Cuttyhunk. Now there's this boat in the book sinking at Monomoy." Her data set forth clearly, she took a deep breath and proposed, "It's all part of cruising—is that it?"

"That's not exactly the way to look—"

"Well," she said, "they were all cruising, and they all sank. That's logic." She broke off and gazed astern. "Maybe you'd better take a look behind."

I did—and saw a curtain of brown fog overtaking us.

Getting a bearing on a standpipe back of Cotuit kept me too busy to hear everything thereafter stated by my bride. But she did opine that not having an engine suited her. "We won't explode," she said, "and I think that's in our favor."

Our sou'west breeze let us thread the hairpin channel into Stage Harbor at Chatham without a tack, but it was foggy that evening, and the following day the fog hung on, making it seem unlikely that we'd soon have a clear day for rounding Monomoy.

At most, I guessed, while we visited friends ashore and heard
the faint "heigh-ho" of distant Stone Horse diaphone, we could
hope for a few hours' visibility. In view of the long beat back
into Nantucket Sound to weather Handkerchief Shoal before a
course for Monomoy could be steered, a few hours seemed
niggardly.

The chart showed a possible shortcut: a narrow strip of deep
water between the tip of Monomoy and the eastward end of
Handkerchief Shoal. If sailable, that channel could save us the
long preliminary beat.

"That's how I take men out to the Lightship," a bo'sun's
mate at the Coast Guard station told me. "From the bell off
Wychmere you lay a course past Monomoy Beach to the lighted
whistle on the main ship channel. Leave that whistle close to
starboard. Rips and eddies will show you where the shoals are."

The following morning came off dark, but whitecaps were
rolling up the harbor before a fresh sou'wester, making fog
seem unlikely. A yacht club launch had offered to tow us outside—another saving in time—and we went down the harbor on
a towline with everything appearing in our favor.

For half a mile along the buoys inside Harding Beach the
gods continued to smile. Then *Little Dipper* came gently to a
halt. So, although its screw churned out a foaming wake, did
the launch ahead.

The language used to inform the launch boy that he'd put
my ship aground, and the language used, while he was getting
her off, to pass judgement on "local knowledge" the world over,
probably startled my new wife. Somewhat uneasily aware of her
presence as progress down channel was resumed, I sought to
justify myself with a description of what "local knowledge"
had done to Voss in the Cocos Islands and what it might just
then have done to us. But her gaze remained troubled, her
dark eyes cloudy, and it seemed plain that she was grappling
with one of Woman's age old problems: how to reconcile the

*Cornet*

Deck layout of *Little Dipper*

snarling tomcat she'd married with the Prince Charming he'd
professed to be.

Then she said earnestly, "Darling, the information the Coast
Guard gave you about this shortcut we're going to take—isn't
that local knowledge too?"

"!*-!!" the tomcat thought, and went forward to check the
towline.

When we'd beat up to Wychmere bell and taken our departure from it, the dark windy morning was turning into a hazy
day. The wind was lightening and the Cape Cod shore astern
was only a blurry profile. Ahead, on a compass course of S¼W,
Monomoy lay invisible beyond a false gray horizon.

Sheets started, we steered a careful course for several miles
until a low, bare strip of sand—Monomoy Beach—came out of
the haze an indefinite distance off the port bow. We held on, the
breeze lightening more, and a cast of the lead showed twenty
feet of water. Another mile or two, and we saw a building on
the beach and found it on the chart: "abandoned lighthouse."
Still further south, the low gray beach appeared to vanish in a
seamless merging of gray sky and sea. Through the binoculars
that ending of the beach looked like our mark, the tip of
Monomoy. Since it lay to leeward of our heading, we put up
the helm and began angling inshore to get on the proper bearing. The ship rolled listlessly and the mainsheet sagged.

I hove the lead: eighteen feet.

Still angling in, we saw tumbled water and gleams of foam
about a mile to the south and reckoned them to be breakers on
Rogers Shoal, the eastern edge of Handkerchief.

When the tip of Monomoy bore S¼W, we sharpened up to
head for it, but our speed through the water did not increase.
The breeze was dying. But the long deserted beach to port, now
less than a mile away and continually closing with our course,
was moving steadily past. The water around us had begun to

lisp and gurgle. With little more than steerage way, we were be-
in hurried along by a strengthening current.

We were playing the sheets, trying to make the most of the
dying breeze, when, looking ahead, I made out the dim shape of
the main channel whistle we'd been told to leave close aboard.
Simultaneously, between us and it, I saw more lumpy water
and more dull gleams of foam. By now the breakers we'd seen
first were abeam to starboard. We were on the course between
Wychmere bell and the channel whistle, but ahead of us and to
starboard frothy water was confusedly tumbling and breaking.
To port was the empty beach.

Rocking, lurching, sails slatting, *Little Dipper* was being carried with increasing speed along the beach toward broken water
there seemed no way of avoiding, and the thought occurred to
me that when we'd altered course and angled in we'd come in
much too close. Had the breakers we'd called Rogers Shoal been
actually the outer breakers off the beach? Were we now inside
them, and in broad daylight steering our ship toward obvious
and certain destruction? If ever water seemed to mark shoals,
the breaking, pyramided water we were heading for seemed to.
The current denied all possibility of turning back.

"We're on the right bearing for the whistle," I said. "We'll
trust the chart and the bo'sun's mate."

My bride looked at me—*and smiled.*

A surge of broken water lifted *Little Dipper*'s bow. Carried
by the current, the ship reared up, hung, and started falling
with broken water splashing along both sides of her hull. Down
went her forebody, plunging deep in foam, and I half expected
a sickening crunch and crack of timbers, a sidewise topple, a
smother of water across the deck.

No sickening crunch, no topple, not a nudge. Her bow came
up and she kept staggering, lurching, rocking forward through
seething rips, eddies, and foot-high overfalls a stone's throw

from the beach. We held our course, and finally had the channel whistle a boat length off the starboard rail.

The chart and the bo'sun's mate had known whereof they spoke: a navigable depth of water does lie between Monomoy and the eastern edge of Handkerchief Shoal. Sail it if your nerves are good—and there is no fog.

As my wife went below to pour us a tot, I wondered what this first cruise of hers would offer next. By the time she re-appeared the answer was plain: puffs and streamers of fog were drifting toward us from the shoals across the ship channel.

Once in the Slue, fog is no great hazard. The current follows the channel, and the channel is lined with bells and whistles. But this fog was cold and dismal.

"Last time I came through this way," I said, "there was a beautiful evening off the Cape. Not a trace of fog, just a violet haze building up along the dunes as the sun went down. The night was full of stars."

My wife sipped her rum, and said, "I'll get the horn out. Three blasts?"

After a chilly night at sea a good sou'wester got up and blew us into Rockport on Cape Ann by early afternoon, but from there to the Isles of Shoals we sailed in fog. From the Shoals we groped through fog to Porpoise, and in cold dark fog past Portland Lightship to Mackerel Cove.

The head got fixed in Boothbay, and from Boothbay we had an honest blue Maine day, crisp and bright, around Pemaquid to an early anchorage among islands in Muscongus Bay. There, as a red sun went down behind a piney skyline, not a sound disturbed a perfect evening calm.

"This," I said, "is Maine!"

But when we put Port Clyde astern and should have opened up the blue heights of the Camden Hills, clouds concealed them. When we made Merchant Row, the pink granite shores of the Row's spruce islands looked colorless in rain.

"From here," I said, after the Mate's smart handling of the headsails had let us pinch and tack the ship through York Narrows in an easterly, "you usually have a wonderful view of Mount Desert." A low overhang hid both Mount Desert and the noble profile of Isle au Haut.

Schoodic, when we rounded it, looked desolate under clouds. At high water the Old Woman sulked invisible beneath a stone gray surface, while to seaward on the Old Man's unmarked, sunken shoulders heavy swells were rearing high and toppling over in cataracts that gleamed like fangs. No bachelor hamburgers, but apples, celery, onions, prologue to chicken *a la Mate*, were sizzling below when we brought the ship to an anchorage off Corea, but the evening was clammy cold. Morning came off calm and thick o' fog—the kind of down east morning some of us somehow delight in—but could my wife? Where were those bright blue mornings I had promised, those hot sunbathing noons?

"We need a breeze to get round Tit Manan," I said. "Maybe we'd better lay over and trade with the natives or something."

"What have you in mind to trade?"

"The sun oil—or my pointed head."

Next day we beat round Tit Manan in fog, and later left Cape Split with clumps and patches of dense fog forming and dissolving in Tabbott Narrows and throughout the seaward islands. Then, as we picked up Black Rock and stood out around Egg Rock and Crumple Island, all fog blew away and ahead of us to the east'ard the granite shores of island after island— Crumple, Freeman's Rock, Steele Harbor—stood up bold and red under a summery blue sky.

"Come up and have a look at down east Maine," I called to the Mate, who was fixing lobster for our lunch. "Today you can really see it!"

When she appeared in the cabin scuttle, she nodded aft. "Take a look astern."

A wall of fog had piled up astern and was moving down on us with giant strides. Late that afternoon, after I'd mistaken a fog-distorted Libby Islands diaphone for the horn at Moose Peak and run right past Moose Peak, we had to jibe over and beat back. Beating back in thick fog, we stood in and out along a roar of breakers pounding on the Head Harbor and Steele Harbor Islands' shores until a ghostly cliff with buildings on it, Moose Peak Light, loomed suddenly out of the fog a hundred feet above us. And then, taking departure from Moose Peak and steering a careful compass course for a quarter mile to Main Channel Way, I twice could not believe that the fog-choked slot in the granite which the compass brought us to could be a sailable channel. Twice I sheered off, and each time breakers came out of the fog ahead and called for a hasty jibe. When, heaving the lead and finding no bottom, I finally braved that box canyon entrance, the girl at the wheel was anxious-eyed and tired.

But the voice that woke me up one morning in the Cow Yard almost sang: "Wake up! Wake up! Santa Claus has come and it's Christmas!"

"Christmas" sure enough: ripples whispered at the planking and the sky framed by the cabin scuttle was a deep and northerly blue.

Reaching gloriously that day, we sailed inside the Brothers. Their steepness and the green turf cradled among their smooth black basalt cliffs made the Mate pronounce them the most dramatic of Maine's islands. Dropping the Libby Islands astern and standing out around Cross Island, we saw Machias Seal to seaward. Miles ahead the cliffs of Grand Manan stood up high and reddish-brown, shimmering in the day's overflow of light.

That night we lay in Cutler, and the fog returned. For two days voices and other shore sounds floated out to our anchored

ship through a dungeon fog in which everything dripped moisture and no air stirred. I began to wonder if we'd ever have
breeze enough to beat back to the westward through the strong
currents that scour that coast.

Wind finally came, with small craft warnings and no thinning of the fog. Anchor up, we groped down the harbor under
staysail and reefed main. At the entrance, loud with the roar of
breakers on rocks we couldn't see, a strong sou'wester heeled us
over and we began a day-long beat—four miles on the offshore
tack, four on the inshore tack to pick up Libby Islands diaphone, then out again into seas steepened by a Bay of Fundy
ebb whose strength we could only guess. That afternoon the
sound of the Moose Peak horn heralded the welcome end of as
trying a thrash to windward in fog, big seas, and current as I
could remember.

"Maine's not always this way," I said for the twentieth time.
This time the Mate scowled.

*Scene*: A cove at Vinalhaven. *Little Dipper* anchored in a
steady rain. Skipper at cabin table silently cursing the un-
relenting weather. Mate sitting up in blankets in her bunk,
reading *The Riddle of the Sands*.

Skipper: "Ordinarily this is one of the prettiest anchorages in
Maine. No houses near and a good berry patch ashore. But this
sure isn't berrying weather. Damn."

Mate continues reading.

More rain.

Skipper: "This is the fifth time I've cruised to Maine, and
it's never been anything like this. Sure, you expect a little fog—
a little's fine. But there've always been lots of blue days. Day
after day, in fact."

Mate: "I've enjoyed our cruise."

Skipper: "Last time I lay in here. . . . What did you say?"

Mate: "I've enjoyed our cruise."

Skipper: "The point is you've come up against the worst summer in twenty years, maybe thirty. I'm going to check when we get home. What you've had is practically unheard-of. That's the point you want to remember. Damn."

Mate: "You have made that point so often that if I do not grasp it now you are married to an idiot."

Skipper: "It's just so you won't get a false impression—"

Mate: "Damn."

Skipper shifts uneasily, sensing shoals ahead.

Mate: "Sometimes I wonder if you really attended our wedding."

Skipper (indignantly): "What d' you mean by that?"

Mate: "Has it ever wriggled into your little pointed head that I'm not just your guest, out for a perfect cruise—whatever that is?"

Skipper's face suggests that maybe it hasn't.

Mate: "I knew before we started we were going to have this kind of weather."

Skipper: "You *knew*?"

Mate: "After the way you talked about Maine all spring, my intuition told me. But I didn't care—*that's* the point! I'm your wife—your *wife*!—and a wife likes being with her husband. Anywhere. Any time. Regardless of the weather. Of all things—the *weather*! *Damn*!"

Now, inside the Skipper's dark interior a light glows and brightens. And the Skipper begins to glimpse, beyond bachelorhood's horizons, wide seas he hasn't sailed . . . (and a way of life secure).

# CHAPTER VII

## Man and Wife to the Caribbean

In June of 1960 well over a hundred yachts manned by large and expert crews put out from Newport, Rhode Island, to race across the Gulf Stream to Bermuda. Two weeks earlier *Little Dipper* had stood out to sea in the same direction—and there the similarity ended.

*Little Dipper* sailed alone, with only my wife and me aboard. The visions luring us into the North Atlantic were not of hard-won trophies but of mountain peaks rising above the blue of tropic ocean, of West Indian islands where people talked with a calypso lilt and sailing vessels still took on passengers and cargos. Come winter, we aimed to cruise the Caribbean.

I'd made the trip before in *Little Dipper* at a severer time of year, but had not done the navigating. In preparation for this trip I read just far enough in Mixter to extract a set of rules for working sun sights. These rules written in a notebook to be followed trained monkey fashion, I began carpentering out more cabin space and building a bang-up chart table. Not unexpectedly, I never got round to actual practice with a sextant.

"Dead reckoning," I said to Lucy, "will probably put us close enough to find Bermuda with the RDF. When we come to close the Virgin Islands I'll have had some practice."

Racing only the hurricane season, we planned to sleep at night. Granted June sou'westers and nothing fiercer than Gulf Stream squalls, we thought basic seamanship might let us make a picnic of the trip's first leg. South of Bermuda much would depend on the Trade Wind's slant.

121

Ashore at Montauk Harbor on the morning of June 4, a phone call to the Weather Bureau encouraged hope for an easy trip. "There's a weak cold front coming through this morning," the forecaster reported. "Otherwise the map's remarkably flat."

"Anything down around the Carolinas that might build up and move out to sea?"

"No indication of it."

Clouds were thickening to the westward as I rowed back to the ship for breakfast. Later, while we were washing dishes, thunder rumbled overhead and the ship yawed at her anchor in a gust of wind and rain. Within minutes the squall had passed. Clearing should follow and might bring a westerly slant helpful to our strategy of sailing south until we reached the Gulf Stream.

But when we ran out between the jetties, clouds still hid the sun and the wind blew from the south. As we reached under the lee of Montauk's moors toward the lighthouse and the open ocean, gusts layed us over and drove us at hull speed with water foaming above the rail.

Beyond the lighthouse Old Ocean, caring nothing for the wind roses shown on pilot charts, met us with a strong south wind. Closehauled, spray flying, we began to drive to windward against gray, cresting rollers that occasionally hove green water across our plunging bow.

"We'd better reef," I said.

Reefing somewhat eased the motion, but when the job was done and Lucy had us sailing full and by, the course I entered in the log as the course that we were making good was a disappointing SE½E. As the bluffs of Montauk shrank astern under a gray overcast, the whitecapped North Atlantic rolling up against our bow looked cold and utterly uncompromising . . .

Late that afternoon the wind had neither eased nor shifted, and we had had our fill of its whine in the rigging and of

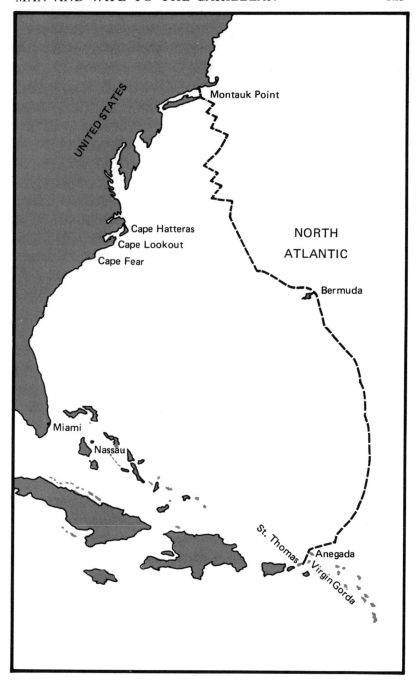

charging seas, spray, and heavy pitching. On the starboard tack
by then and slugging out a disappointing WxS, we half backed
the staysail, rigged a radar reflector in the shrouds, and went
below, leaving the ship to work her own way through the seas.
Both of us were soaked and cold. I had tossed my lunch and did
not eat much supper.

That night the wind moderated, and dawn revealed thick fog
drifting across a sloppy sea. We shook out our reef and hoisted
the masthead jib, but the breeze stayed in the south, grew sluggish, and moved us only slowly.

When I put my head out the scuttle next morning, a big sea
off the starboard bow had reared its bulk against a low gray sky
and was hurling a breaking crest down on us. The persistent
head wind was once more singing in the shrouds. By noon of
this, our third day at sea, dead reckoning placed us less than a
hundred miles to the south of Montauk.

In view of the tacks we'd made, dead reckoning was only a
guess, but our need to make southing was so obvious that it
didn't seem worthwhile to try for sextant sights. I supposed that
even with a clear sky my first attempt to get a sun line by the
directions in my notebook might take several hours. We continued tacking southward and took all night in.

The free wind we'd been waiting for ended a calm through
which we'd slept our fourth night out. Before the sun got up
that morning I had all sail hoisted. When Lucy handed breakfast up, the ship was running nicely across a smooth sea rippled
by a gentle norther. The sun rose big and warm. From horizon
to horizon the water was a brilliant Gulf Stream blue.

An hour later our radio brought in WWV's time tick loud
and clear. I broke out my sextant and came on deck with it, a
stopwatch, and a pencil.

Watching me as I sat down on the cabin top and arranged my
arcane tools, Lucy said, "I should have made you a tall hat with

stars and half moons on it—like the Professor in the Katzen-jammer Kids."

"This," I replied, "is Science. Or supposed to be."

Glancing port and starboard across the empty ocean, she murmured that her interest in the experiment equalled mine.

The sun came into the mirror and down to the horizon more easily than I'd expected. I took six sights at intervals of one minute and was pleased to see that the altitudes showed a constant increase. Then I went below and started work with notebook, Almanac, HO 214, a pad of Mixter's navigation forms—and an eraser. About an hour later, with the eraser somewhat worn, I had an Assumed Position, an azimuth, and an intercept.

"Did it work?" Lucy asked when I came on deck.

"We've got to wait for noon."

Waiting as the ship ran on across a sunlit ocean, I reflected on a number of facts which hour by hour seemed more impressive: (1) in thinking that dead reckoning would put us close enough to Bermuda to pick up the island's radio, I'd had sou'west winds and a straightish course in mind—and we'd done hell's own amount of tacking; (2) once I'd plotted my two sun lines and got their intersection, there'd be no checking the result in the back of any book; (3) when I *had* checked my working of practice problems, some mighty dreary errors had turned up.

We tried to catch noon by the sun's approach to a bearing of true south, but when I began observing with the sextant the sun was losing altitude. Thankful that modern navigation made a noon sight non-essential, I took another string of altitudes and went below.

"If it doesn't work," I called up to the helmsman, "we can always find America."

"My ticket reads Bermuda," she replied.

This time the arithmetic went a little faster, but when I'd plotted the two sun lines and sat staring at their intersection, deep scepticism arose. That the alleged fix placed us some sixty miles closer to Bermuda than my DR caused no great surprise. Beating, I usually take a gloomy view of what course my ship is making good. But that a sextant worked by me could accurately measure the sun's height, that my arithmetic contained no flaws,

The Wife

that a raw first-timer could find his position on this whirling planet by squinting at a sun ninety million miles away—*that* called for more credulity than a coastwise fog-runner trained to believe nothing until he saw, heard, smelled, or grounded on it could muster. I wrote the supposed position in the log—37 37 N 69 55 W, but saved self-respect by labelling the figures "*Damn*

*Dubious.*" Then I went on deck and reported them to the crew.

"I expect," she said, "that's just where we are!"

By now our northerly breeze had veered and freshened. Throwing a crisp bow wave, we were reaching smoothly under a deep blue sky. All signs of cloud had vanished. The barometer was rising. Although the breeze came from the east, it felt dry and cool against our faces. A high seemed to have moved in. It might well see us through the Stream.

The breeze slowly freshened throughout the afternoon. Under mainsail and both headsails *Little Dipper* took increasing heel, and the log swinging abaft the helmsman showed that the ship was moving across the ocean at a nice six knots. The sun went down red and round, and though the sea was getting up the wind's increase was greater, giving the ship a drive that made the water foaming past feel smooth. Telling me to call her if I wanted a relief, Lucy yawned off to bed. Soon a bright moon rose, silvering the dark surface of the ocean, and through the early night hours *Little Dipper* steadily increased her speed until she was hurtling through beam seas at seven knots, then better, rail down and bow wave roaring. She had seldom sailed so fast so smoothly. The roar and power of her forward rush across the moonlit ocean produced a rare elation and kept me at the wheel till midnight. When I finally hauled down the jib and main and left her fore-reaching under staysail only, I logged the wind at twenty knots, NE, and knew I'd had a sail I would remember.

Below, an uneasy murmur came from Lucy's bunk.

"Thought you'd gone to sleep," I said.

"Down here it sounded as if she was going to tear the keel off!"

She wasn't likely to do that, but when I pumped the bilge before turning in I found she'd made a good deal of water.

At dawn the northeast wind was blowing harder. The sky had

clouded over and the sea had roughened. But the barometer had not fallen and a northeast wind was fair. We tied in a reef and reached through increasing wind and rising seas till noon, when I judged the wind was blowing thirty knots. The ship was sailing fast and still steering well, but the seas crowding up abeam were beginning to look like hills. Their breaking crests left streaks of foam in deepening troughs. A gale in June seemed most unlikely, but why risk damage to sails or rigging when in all probability the wind would moderate soon? June's sou'westers were long overdue. We lowered the main, stowed the boom in its gallows, and, to be forehanded, hove to under a storm trysail.

During the night rain began a steady drumming on the dinghy lashed above the skylight. At dawn, although the barometer had gone down only one tenth of an inch, the voice of the wind had gained a booming resonance. That sound, and the heavy motion of the ship as I struggled into oilskins and my safety belt, warned that we had been overtaken by a gale.

When I had climbed into the heeling cockpit and was hanging to the boom in driving rain and rushing wind, it was evident that while we'd slept mighty forces had swung into action. Under a low dark sky the seas were hills indeed. When we dropped into their troughs they swelled up to windward higher than our spreaders and were topped by breaking crests, here and there by curled, unbroken lips of livid blue. *Little Dipper* rose to one of these seas, and as it swept off to leeward, veils of spindrift scurried along its white-streaked back.

The wind, I thought, was blowing about forty knots and gusting higher. In June it wasn't likely to blow much harder, but its slow buildup over the previous two days wasn't cheering to remember.

"It took a long time coming," I said when I went below. "It may be a long time going."

We were hove to on the port tack, and since an easterly gale coming in on a high barometer will often back, we decided to leave her as she was. Sometimes raising hopes that it would moderate, then blowing harder, the gale sang through our rigging and kept us heeled and tossing all that day. The ship rode well enough, but rain and occasional crests striking her abeam searched out openings in the skylight and created a clammy shambles below. The only comfort, the only place in the lurching cabin where one did not have to grip a handhold to stay put, was in the bunks. There we lay. Lucy read while I, coddling my stomach, forebore to read and glumly stared at the dripping skylight and thought the dark thoughts small boat sailors think in gales. Confident of my stomach by afternoon, I too began to read—and soon had to climb on deck and hang my head over the coaming. Whereupon my thoughts grew darker still.

Instead of let-up, evening brought an increase in the wind. The barometer edged down, the crests slamming into the port bow seemed to strike the planking more fiercely than before, and I began to be concerned about the amount of water the ship was making.

I'd had the ship surveyed before we left. We'd backed out and examined half a dozen fastenings on each side, and found them sound. But for the last two days, as the gale built up, she'd required more and more strokes of the pump. Now, as the night wore on, I pumped at regular intervals, and found the number of strokes increasing.

Leaks are queer. A leak may warn that a weakened frame or butt block is ready to let a plank go, while another leak may mean only that sound keel bolts need taking up or that seams between dried out upper strakes are not, when the ship is continuously and deeply heeled, as tight as you might wish. When you're riding out a gale at sea it's hard to know what kind of leak you're up against. Much of the night I lay awake pondering this interesting question. Across the lamplit, half-dark cabin Lucy seemed asleep, but probably wasn't. The wind howled aloft, the ship staggered under the blows of breaking crests, and dawn seemed a long time coming.

Dawn's light revealed undiminished seas still heaving their ragged tops toward low bulging clouds. The wind was still northeast, still booming.

"Let's try easing her," I said. "We'll put a warp over the stern, take in the trysail, and run her off before it."

For an hour we ran that way, making only slow progress but not thinking it wise to try for any speed in seas towering up above our transom and sweeping under us with frequent roars of tumbling foam. Then, unattracted by the prospect of a cold wet day behind the wheel with no real mileage gained, we decided to see if she'd lie more easily under bare pole than under the trysail. Finding a comparatively smooth patch astern, we rounded up. She lost way and lay beam to the seas, leaving a good smooth dead to windward. After lashing the helm, I went below and pumped her dry.

An hour later I pumped her again, and was greatly cheered to find she'd made much less water than during the hours of the night. Evidently her greater heel under the trysail, or the greater strain that sail imposed on hull and chain plates, had had something to do with her abnormal leakage. At any rate, we had an answer to it. Although we'd had her practically stopped under the trysail, lying under bare pole she took fewer hard knocks, owing no doubt to the windward smooth.

Toward noon the wind began to back and moderate. The clouds thinned, and miles away to port we saw shafts of sunlight angling down and throwing metallic gleams upon the heaving wilderness of water. Thinking the gale was blowing itself out, we put up the helm and again ran off to the southward, this time not towing a warp. Soon I gave the wheel to Lucy and went forward to hoist the staysail. It snapped and bellied out to a strong nor'wester, and the ship began making knots at last. We were thinking of hoisting a deep reefed main when the wind suddenly increased its force and a white squall whirled up astern. The wind's thrum in the rigging rose to an eerie squeal. We heeled over and drove, rail down, ploughing up a bow wave, through seas once more veiled in spindrift.

Heartily sick of lying to, we left the staysail on her, kept the wind on the quarter, and ran for an hour at a speed the log advised was seven knots. At the end of that time, the sky was growing darker and the seas were building up higher than ever. Even the staysail seemed too much.

Thanks to the downhaul we had fitted for the passage, the staysail came in easily. Spelling each other at the wheel, we continued to run off with cresting seas heaving their tons of water high above the counter and swiftly passing under us.

We were running so with Lucy at the wheel, when, after an attempt to bring our DR up to date, I emerged from the cabin and saw a sea coming up astern which I knew at once would poop us. As seas went that day, it was a small one, but its overtaking face was impossibly steep, a nearly vertical wall of unbroken water. *Little Dipper* tried to rise to it, but its top burst right across the counter, threw Lucy against the wheel, filled the cockpit, and streamed forward along the decks.

Lucy was unhurt and courageously kept the ship on course, but we took the incident as a friendly warning from Old Ocean of what could happen if one of the really big seas mountaining up behind us should decide to steepen as that little one had.

Once more we brought her up, lashed the helm down, and let her lie a-try.

It blew a gale all night, and there was little change the following day. Aside from that one pooping sea, which had been small, we'd seen nothing that looked really dangerous. The wind was not as fierce, nor the seas as high, as in a November gale which *Little Dipper* had ridden out while making the same passage five years before. But this gale seemed resolved to last forever. A bigger crew could have run her through most or all of it, but we could not arrange the reliefs of the helm which would have made running bearable. As in any gale outside the tropics, the helmsman soon became not only wet but cold. On this gale's third day we again tried running under bare pole, but soon decided that the misery of shivering in wet clothes wasn't worth the progress made.

We heard later that two Bermuda yachts bound for Newport with racing crews had encountered this same heavy weather. Sailing for one period of fourteen hours at hull speed under storm jib only, *Undina* made a fast passage. *Chicane*, a fifty-six footer, was blown a hundred miles off course.

Toward dark I clambered from my bunk to have a look at the sky and sea, and when I looked out the scuttle was startled to see the towering broadside of a steamer about a cable length to windward. A few passengers were hanging to her deck rails, watching us, and an officer stood on the wing of her bridge observing us through binoculars.

Joining me on the companionway steps, Lucy caught her breath at sight of the nearby monster.

"It's OK," I began. "He know's what he's doing—"

"My hair!" she murmured—and stepped back down, found a comb, and then, prepared for company, rejoined me at the scuttle.

I gave the steamer a wave and my wife a public hug and kiss.

The steamer sheered off and disappeared into the dusk, talking to itself.

That night the wind moderated, and on our ninth morning at sea, at long, long last, we began to get the sou'westerlies proper to the time of year. Soon after dawn we were making five knots under the staysail with wind and sea fast going down. A little later the main was on her and she was reaching across big but smoothly rounded seas at a good six knots. The sky cleared. Sunshine warmed us and dried off patches of the salt-crusted deck. By 0800 we were sailing across a summer ocean and wondering what course would bring us "Where the remote Bermuda's ride In the ocean's bosom unespied."

I took a morning sight, caught the sun's hang at noon for latitude, and came up with a position: 34 18 N 67 02 W. That put us some hundred and sixty miles from St. David's Head and in position to make a fair wind of a sou'wester. But could my navigation be trusted? I tinkered with the RDF and soon heard Radio Bermuda.

"The bearing tallies with my fix!" I told the crew.

She looked at me respectfully.

That evening, when we sat in the cockpit to enjoy our grog, we'd had a day of highly welcome, pleasant sailing.

I stayed at the wheel till midnight, while a bright moon climbed the sky and gilded the edges of thin wisps of cloud. The ship slid smoothly through the darkened sea and rolled easily as dying swells passed under her. This was the ocean and the sailing one expects in June, and nothing can be more enjoyable. Reluctantly at length, I took in the main and jib, trimmed the staysail a few inches a-weather, lashed the helm, and went below. While we slept *Little Dipper* faithfully kept the wind abeam and logged twenty-one miles.

My next noon fix put us less than sixty miles from Bermuda. Encouraged by its tallying with the radio, we decided to trust it and shape a course from it to the island's entrance. This meant peeling off from the radio bearing—the station was no doubt in Hamilton—and bringing that bearing more and more abeam. We no sooner peeled off than the scepticism by which a coastwise pilot lives and keeps his bottom smooth awoke and took me by the throat. I'd cut a sorry figure if we sailed right past the island and had to hunt for it upwind.

I stood behind the wheel most of the afternoon, steering with my knees to keep both hands free to scour the horizon with the binoculars.

Lucy offered to take the wheel and let me nap.

"Not sleepy," I muttered, scouring.

"According to the log we've still got thirty miles to go!"

"Unh-hunh," I muttered, and kept looking.

I steered (more or less) and searched—ahead in hope, abeam in blackest pessimism. Four tropic birds suddenly came out of nowhere and circled the masthead, but the ship sailed on across an empty ocean.

Suddenly, through the binoculars, a white and steady spot appeared on the horizon off the starboard bow. For several minutes it seemed like land, perhaps a cliff that faced the westering sun, but it rapidly grew larger and became a steamer's bridge. The steamer's hull followed it up over the horizon and soon was passing us a mile abeam, but not, so far as I could judge, on a course parallel and opposite to ours. Surely a steamer so close to Bermuda would have called there and have it dead astern. This one seemed to have come from far upwind of the direction we were steering for. It vanished down the horizon.

A bad sign, I thought. Very damn bad . . .

The breeze was freshening and drawing ahead.

Lucy's head appeared in the scuttle. "Supper's almost ready. I think you ought to come below. We won't be in before dark anyway."

I trimmed the main and staysail to let the ship sail herself, and gloomily went below. "This navigating business seemed to be working," I said, "but according to that steamer we're headed for St. Helena."

"How do you know the steamer came from Bermuda?"

"I don't. But it probably did. Because that's the way things work."

"I've never seen you fret so!"

"Who? Me?"

"Here's your drink."

By the time we'd finished eating, the sky framed by the scuttle was dark and peppered with stars. The ship had begun to

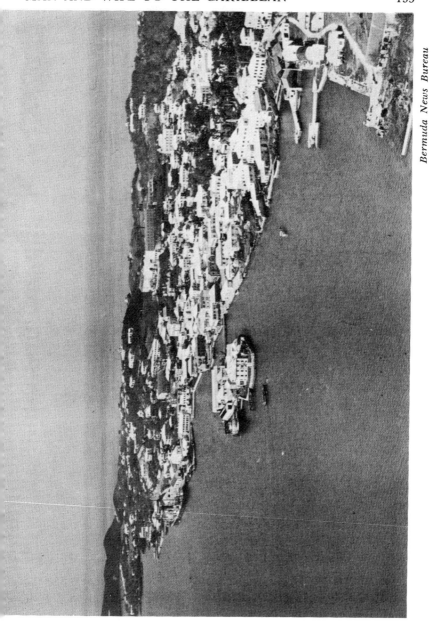

*Bermuda News Bureau*

St. George, Bermuda

lift and settle to a rising sea. I climbed the companionway and shoved head and shoulders out the scuttle.

Astern: only the splashing blackness of a nighttime ocean. Port and starboard: more splashing and more blackness. I leaned farther out to peer forward around the dinghy, and there, fine on the starboard bow and low down across miles of darkly gleaming water, a dozen lights were shining. Where they shone, the starlit sky profiled a dark unmoving lump of land.

"Sort of an interesting sight up here," I said. "Come have a look."

When we let go our anchor off St. George's the following morning, two sailing vessels moored to the town quay caught our eyes. The entirely housed in cockpit of the smaller one—we judged her length to be twenty feet—and the other's bulwarks and heavy rigging suggested both were owned by ocean cruising folk. Ironically, by the time we'd rowed to the quay, singlehanders aboard both these vessels were casting off their dock lines. We climbed onto the quay, joined a crowd of onlookers, and learned that the bigger vessel had come in from the Bahamas and was shoving off for Florida. The tiny one had been built by her owner in South Africa and by him sailed up across the South Atlantic. He was leaving now for England.

While we watched, the larger ship tossed a towline to the tiny one. They filed off toward Town Cut and, beyond that narrow passage, the wide Atlantic.

"The little one," said Lucy, "looks awfully little!"

My answer conveyed the respect someone who has bought his boat feels for someone who has built his own. "The man's a *sailor!*"

A few days later we had better luck with Don Street, another *sailor*. We awoke to find his sizeable cutter anchored near, and by afternoon Don—a tiny man with a luxuriant golden beard—was gamming with us in *Little Dipper*'s cockpit. Don's ship, and only share of this world's goods, was the *Iolaire,* an ancient English fifty-footer. With a couple of islanders to help him, Don had performed the considerable feat of raising her from the bottom of a Virgin Island bay and re-building a stove-in side. He was taking her and a crew of friends to New York, where he hoped sailorizing jobs and charters would bring in cash enough to let him sail for England. Beyond that he seemed to have no plans. He needed none. The sea was his wife and home. Perched on our cockpit coaming in the ragged shirt and shorts he'd worn on his passage from St. Thomas, telling us of the conditions he'd encountered, he looked—small stature, beard, and raggedness—like a knowing sea-elf, Neptune's emissary, washed ashore by a passing wave.

*Iolaire* had come up from St. Thomas in the fast time of six days, and the information that the Trade had blown with a southerly slant all the way to 27 North strengthened my intention of getting well to the eastward while still in the westerlies near Bermuda. Five years earlier, in early winter, summer slants had not concerned us. Now, with June almost gone, I laid out a course which would put us one hundred and thirty miles to the east of the Bermuda-St. Thomas rhumb line by the time we reached 27 North. From there I planned to hold that easting south to 23 North and only then bear off for the Virgin Islands.

That course would bring us in past Anegada, a low island without a lighthouse, and unmarked Horseshoe Reef, whose full wickedness comes clear when you see it on a chart, curving out from Anegada for fifteen miles. In clear weather the high peak of Virgin Gorda should come up over the horizon well before we closed Anegada or Horseshoe Reef, but squalls and darkness had to be considered. The course presented dangers, but, remembering how boisterously the Trade could blow, I wanted to make sufficient easting to be able eventually to ease off and start sheets. Almost anything beats holding a small boat up to windward through five hundred miles of Trade Wind seas.

Hoping to tighten up our hull, we took up on several keel bolts, removed some slack from the lower shrouds, and re-chocked our inside ballast. These jobs did not take long, but having a spray hood made and fitted took the best part of ten days. We still were waiting for the spray hood when the blow that hit the 1960 Bermuda Race fleet came through. It made me roll out of a warm bunk to tend dock lines, but moderated the following day. The incidents such a short blow caused among the racing fleet, all of them carrying all possible sail, empha-sized the difference between racing and cruising seamanship. Men overboard, dismastings—these cannot be risked on a wind-jammer cruising shorthanded and alone.

Racing yachts were still coming over a squally horizon to the north when we took our departure from St. David's Head at noon, June 24th, and started reaching SSE in a sou'west breeze. At noon next day a latitude crossed with a radio bearing put us more than a hundred miles toward our first turning point at 27 North, but the breeze was failing. By evening we rolled be-calmed on an ocean turning glassy and moved only by a lazy swell. No air stirred that night. On deck, with our pressure lan-tern slung in the rigging, we had an eerie impression that the ship lay anchored in some uncharted harbor whose shores lay just beyond the lantern's glare. The roll almost stopped. No sound disturbed the quiet night.

Morning came off sunny with a faint air out of the east, and *Little Dipper* ghosted under all sail through smooth water that was deeply penetrated by rays from a brilliant sun. A glance down past the rail into the lighted water was startling. Vision plunged down, deep after deep, through a blue transparency that seemed far too insubstantial to float our weight of wood and metal. Staring down through those lighted depths brought a dizzying reminder of how high and condor-like above the ocean floor—higher than Mount Whitney's peak above Death Valley—our little ship was sailing.

For an hour or more we watched a school of trigger fish and two or three small dolphin travelling with us in the jewel-like water beside the hull. The dolphin foraged restlessly, often

*Bermuda News Bureau*

St. David's Head

darting out of sight to port or starboard, but so far as we could see not catching anything. The trigger fish, little fellows in the plank-on-edge tradition, occasionally heeled over to look up at us with bulging eyes, but mostly saved their strength for when the ship passed near a clump of floating weed. Then they raced each other to the weed and snapped and tore voraciously at whatever tiny creatures nested among the twigs and berries. Once one tiny creature, which we could not identify, broke to the surface and went tearing off in a series of frantic leaps. The smooth limpid water offered no concealment all the way to the horizon, and the fastest trigger fish soon caught and ate him.

High above this display of nature's government—merciless if looked at from a point of view unknown to trigger fish and tiny creatures—the sun shone benignly in a hot blue sky.

Although by noon that day the air had freshened, our twenty-four hour run was only sixty miles. And the breeze had moved into the southeast.

"I can't believe," I said, "we picked up the Trade at thirty North."

Trade or not, we had seen the last of the westerlies. When the sun went down that evening its last rays reached toward the zenith behind a fleet of low, dark-bottomed Trade Wind clouds. The ship was hard on the wind, beginning to pitch as we tried to make our easting.

"This day dawns with scattered squalls," I wrote in the log next morning. "Hard on the wind and can't get E," was the entry a few hours later. Sure that the Trade would strengthen as we sailed farther south, and hoping to enjoy a day or two of that quartering off which is the cream of ocean cruising, we held up to the freshening wind and chopped out easting when we could, while the ship pitched heavily and sometimes drove her bowsprit into whitecapped seas. All that day and for two more like it, for some three hundred miles, we pitched and butted our way southward, decks streaming and deeply heeled, through ocean seas that hove us skyward, then dropped us roughly down.

"How about a chicken fricasee," my tough-stomached wife inquired, "with rice and cranberry sauce?"

"I think," I answered, "I'll stick to soup and cheese and crackers."

Finally a noon fix at the end of our fifth day out showed that we had made our planned easting.

"Lay her off a couple of points," I called up from the chart table, and the next log entry read, "A fine afternoon with the ship sailing fast on a nice beam reach. What a difference two points makes!"

Instead of slowly clambering up the seas and tumbling down as they passed under, instead of treating us to shock and lurch and stagger, *Little Dipper* now went swinging off across the rolling ocean at a steady ocean-eating speed. In the daytime the cabin was hot, and the spray hood proved a boon in an unexpected way, keeping out heat and glare. On deck the wind kept us comfortable. Although we continued taking the nights in, our daily runs began to average a hundred and twenty miles.

By now the sun shone directly overhead at noon and my dependence on sun lines for finding our position revealed unexpected limitations. At noon the sun changed his bearing so rapidly that I couldn't tell what part of the horizon to bring him down to. Worse, as we sailed south of the sun, the sun bore eighty-odd degrees east all morning, eighty-odd degrees west all afternoon. On July 1 all my sun lines turned out roughly parallel, giving no decent cut. Latitude sights became essential. Directions for working one star, Polaris, were in my notebook.

As twilight fell that evening Polaris turned up in the sky astern, but was only a blurry pinpoint in the sextant mirror. I recorded a doubtful sight, and had to break off trying for a better one at the approach of a squall we had been watching for some time. At a distance it had been a white-topped cloud towering hugely above the darkening ocean. Now, as it bore down on us, its top still gleaming far above us, it developed a nasty leading edge, close to the water and jet black. Glowering at us, this black edge came on. It struck with a fierce gust of wind and a torrent of rain. The ship heeled over and went charging off like a runaway torpedo through solid rain and utter blackness.

A half hour later the sea was smooth and Polaris shone clearly in the sextant mirror, but the horizon was dark and vague. I sat a long time on the cabin top, squinting through the sextant, taking discrepant altitudes, not sure of any. And then it dawned on me that the uncertain twists I was giving my micrometer were ones of no more than three minutes. I went below and checked my notebook. "One minute of arc," it read, "equals one mile."

Far at sea, who cares about three miles? Not *Little Dipper*.

I rolled off to sleep with more enthusiasm than ever for an art that even in poor conditions told a beginner all he had to know.

But he had best use caution. By morning I calculated we were some hundred and twenty miles from Anegada, and the wind was blowing fresh. All day, with sheets taut, sails bellying, and our wake streaming aft at six or seven knots, the dangers of our landfall grew more imposing. Anegada was low, unlighted, ten miles long. According to the SAILING DIRECTIONS it could never be seen more than six miles off. Horseshoe Reef was unlighted and unmarked. Seas broke all along its fifteen mile length. Breakers often can't be seen from upwind until you're in them. Both these dangers rose abruptly from deep water.

I succeeded in taking a noon latitude and thereby got a fix, but wasn't sure how far to trust a latitude taken with the sun so close to overhead. Later I shot the sun again, and at twilight observed Polaris for another fix. We hove to early, trimming the sails to stop the ship instead of keep her sailing, and according to my calculations thirty miles of ocean still rolled between us and Anegada's beach. When a final observation of Polaris checked out with the others, I saw no reason not to go to sleep.

Morning came off cloudy with the clouds thickest to the south. DR said a course of WSW would send us safely past the western end of Anegada, and we bore off along that course, quartering off before the wind for the first time, except in squall or gale, since we'd left New England.

"We should be well within the arc of Virgin Gorda's visibility," I said sometime later. But clouds were still thick to the southwest and south. The ship was moving fast, surging in big gray quartering seas.

Below, Lucy tinkered with the radio and heard a station announcement from San Juan. A radio bearing taken from a little ship yawing and rolling in a seaway cannot be anything but coarse, but by the bearing we seemed well to the north of wicked Horeshoe Reef.

The ship ran on. Behind us and to seaward patches of sunlight lighted up the tumbling ocean, but to port and ahead, where we expected to see Anegada or, fifteen miles behind it, the peak of Virgin Gorda, low shifting clouds obscured the horizon and the sky.

A bird flew past. His markings and swooping flight identified him as a booby, a bird that usually returns to land at night.

Temporarily the clouds away off on the port bow thinned, and behind them loomed a ghostly dark blue bulk, well above the water. Blue with distance, veiled by thinning streaks of cloud, that bulk became a mountain rising steeply to a peak. Then those streaks of cloud grew thicker. Peak and mountain blurred. But where they'd been that ghostly dark blue bulk still loomed through the clouds.

"Land Ho!" I shouted. "Blow me down if it isn't Virgin Gorda!"

We sailed on, and the horizon ahead was suddenly speckled with black unmoving dots, the brushtops of Anegada. The sky was clearing as Anegada's yellow beach slid past half a mile to port. Anegada fell astern, and we hardened up a bit, leaving the ocean's blue behind us and sailing into the shoal green water on the Virgin Island bank. Now Virgin Gorda stood up clear and blue on our port hand, and we sailed southwest toward more blue mountains twenty miles ahead. A passing squall brought rain, and we pulled off salt-stiff sea clothes, let warm fresh water stream down us, and felt wonderfully refreshed.

Running between Tortola's steep green mountainsides and those of Jost van Dyke, *Little Dipper* ran as steady as a train. The mountains standing up on every hand, the white beaches at their feet, a laden cargo sloop ahead, frigate birds soaring in the sky's soft blue, testified to the fifteen hundred miles our ship had put astern. We'd sailed her into the tropics, for us a far part of the world. Come snow and cold at home, we'd raise more mountain landfalls and lie at anchor in warm harbors off sea-faring towns.

That, we found out, wasn't all. We hadn't sailed for trophies, but that evening in St. Thomas we knew we'd won the finest prizes small boat sailing offers man and wife: reliance on each other, freedom of the seas.

# CHAPTER VIII

## Short Tacks Here and There

By no means the least attraction of cruising is that you can look forward to enjoying the best of it and being able to take the worst even when you're well along in years. At the age of eighty-two Martin Kattenhorn was cruising off Cape Cod in his fine old gaff-rigged schooner *Surprise* when Hurricane Carol swept up the coast. With Mrs. Kattenhorn and an Italian gardener for crew, *Surprise*'s seasoned skipper rode out that killer storm at sea. For years thereafter the Kattenhorns turned up regularly at Stonington, cruising still, as always without an engine, and still, by the look of *Surprise* as she lay at anchor with her topsail neatly brailed, cruising smartly. The last time I saw *Surprise* she was heading east through Watch Hill Passage in a dungeon fog, breaking out her topsail.

Though barely out of rompers by Martin Kattenhorn's high standards, Dr. Clermont Grantham-Hill of England was a respectable sixty-six years old when he, his son, and a seventeen year old hand sailed the cutter *Windstream* from Marseilles across the Atlantic to the West Indies and Florida. Coasting north past Charleston, it occurred to the Doctor that he hadn't seen Bermuda, and he stood blithely out to sea to repair that omission. On arrival in New York after nine days of head winds he quipped that sailing was "virtually a breeze." There may be sixty-six year old tennis players who can hold their own in national tournaments, a rough equivalent of the Doctor's voyaging, but who would bet on it?

Surely the reason cruising stays accessible to men whose step has shortened is that, in cruising, know-how plays so large a part. No other sport demands one-quarter as much sheer knowledge: design, construction, ship handling in all weathers, piloting, marlinspike seamanship, painting, sewing, carpentry, metalwork, plumbing, meteorology, celestial navigation, cooking. A golfer can win the National Open and know not a tenth as much, which is no doubt why he finds himself a has-been at age fifty. A small boat sailor need not plumb every branch of sea-going science to its depths (as he may count on some day plumbing his toilet), but over the years he can't help accumulating an impressive store of knowledge. This will earn him welcome aboard any ship long after he cares to take in headsails with green water breaking over him, long after he's physically able to tarzan up a swaying mast at sea.

Such, at least, were my reflections one morning in St. Thomas after sighting a little double-ended cutter that looked familiar at the Coast Guard quay. Strolling down the quay to make her re-acquaintance, I thought I remembered her name, *Viking*, and her owner's, John Wendes. As I came up astern of her the back of a bald head was visible at her scuttle.

From the quay alongside her cockpit I verified my man by his pointed moustaches and long, forked beard.

"Didn't we meet in Halifax last June?" I asked.

John looked up at me with his blue eyes crinkled against the morning sunlight. In a moment he grinned and boomed in a Swedish accent, "You vere aboard dot oshun razor!"

The previous June, *Viking* had caught my eye when she entered Halifax while that harbor was crowded with the Marblehead-to-Halifax racing fleet. She put down her anchor abeam of the racer I was on, and her short rig, the spare spars lashed on her deck, her heavy plough steel rigging, and, not least, the look of her lanky, bald, fork-bearded skipper hinted she was going places. I took a dinghy alongside her, and a gam proved I'd guessed right. From Halifax *Viking* was bound for St. John's,

*Belfast Telegraph*

John Wendes' Yacht *Viking*

John Wendes

Newfoundland, and from there to Sweden via the Orkney Islands. Some trip.

Now I asked, "How were the Orkney Islands?"

"Come aboard!" John boomed. "I tell you efryt'ing. But virst ve drink chartreuse!" He waved a bare, tattooed arm. "Green or yallow—ve got bot'!"

Below, chartreuse in hand, I met his crew and learned that *Viking* had just blown in from Las Palmas, Canary Islands. After making Sweden as planned, John had cruised the Baltic, then run down the Channel, across the Bay of Biscay, and so out to Las Palmas, across the Atlantic, and that morning into St. Thomas.

Between Las Palmas and St. Thomas, a crew member told me, a jib halyard had parted. John himself had gone to the masthead to reeve off a new one.

"How old is he?" I asked.

"Seventy-one."

John waved a liqueur bottle at me. "Green or yallow? Ve got bot'!"

From Cape Porpoise, Maine, to the Isles of Shoals is ordinarily an easy jump for a harbor-hopper, but light airs and fog can complicate it. One September morning *Little Dipper* took a departure from Cape Porpoise in a nice sou'wester, but got becalmed toward noon. By evening the light easterly breeze which followed the calm had brought us no further than the lighted whistle six miles off Portsmouth, New Hampshire. As the whistle fell astern, a fog rolled in and quickly transformed twilight into thick damp night.

Her main close hauled between her running lights' dim, colored auras, *Little Dipper* slipped quietly through black invisibility. The compass light showed we were laying the course to the Isles, but a trip below to study the chart indicated we could expect to do some piloting before we found the harbor in the middle of them. Approaching from the north in an easterly air, we likely would not hear the horn on White Island, southernmost of the Isles. Nor, until we were on it, could we hope to hear the harbor bell. We'd have to bring her in without the help of government aids to navigation.

"Let's eat now," I said.

Supper eaten and cleared away, the cabin lamp put out to prevent disturbing glare from the scuttle, *Little Dipper* slid through the dark with only a rippling at her bow, an occasional creak of blocks, breaking the thick silence.

"What's the log say?" I asked my crew.

"Twenty-four," he read with a flashlight's aid. "Maybe a shade over."

About half a mile, I reckoned, to where we ought to have Duck Island close abeam to port. Unless a current had set us east or west. In daylight I'd seen current running among the Isles and off them, but had never worked out a way of predicting it.

"Let's heave the lead."

The lead clunked into water.

"No bottom at forty feet," my crew reported.

"O.K."

"On the chart," he said, "Duck Island's nasty. Rocks and ledges all around it."

"Don't talk. Listen."

The ship ghosted on through thick wet air and velvet blackness. Listening hard, I heard only our bow ripple and the sea's faint whispering.

Barring current set, we were coming up on Duck Island from its leeward side, where there would probably be little surf. But if what I'd remarked on previous visits to the Isles still held true, the sound of surf would be superfluous.

Through the fog off the port bow came a sound. It came again—a faint discordant clamor.

"Birds," I murmured. "That's Duck Island."

The sound grew louder—did birds ever sleep?—and drew abeam to port.

"Read the log."

"Twenty-five."

The sound of birds faded away into the blackness astern and once more we heard only the liquid murmur of our passage through the water, an occasional slat of sail, the sea's low whisper. We were safely past Duck Island.

The ship ghosted on for five minutes, ten, fifteen, and as I was about to ask for another reading of the log we heard more birds ahead.

"That's Appledore."

Appledore's shore being bolder than Duck Island's, I held up through the fog toward our insomniac feathered friends until, amid their clamor, we distinguished individual squawks and cries. Then I eased off to skirt the shore with what sounded like a reasonable offing.

It wasn't long before we heard a lazy clang of the bell off Gosport Harbor. In the calm sea, clangs were few, but frequent enough to guide us.

Such little successes are pleasant to remember . . .

As many a northern yachtsman has discovered, the Caribbean Trade Wind bears scant resemblance to the "balmy breezes" in Caribbean travel folders. The Trade blows hard, seldom less than fifteen knots and often thirty, and in the open ocean off West Indian Islands a breeze of that strength builds up hefty seas. Cruising the Islands, you come to feel that here, if anywhere, you want strong sails and rigging. Feeling so, when you first look closely at the little ships which year by year of all little ships in the world put the most blue water behind them, the cargo-carrying sloops native to the Islands, you'll be horrified.

You'll approve their heavy, rock-ballasted hulls. Or if you

don't you ought to, because these hulls regularly carry cargos for two generations of owners. Also, there's much to be said for their leg o' mutton sail plans, with low raked masts stepped well into the hulls, permitting goodsized foretriangles. But their long overhanging booms will make you lift an eyebrow, particularly when you see that these long booms are usually two crude spars crudely scarphed, the scarph wrapped with rusty wire. You'll do more than lift an eyebrow when you look at shrouds and forestays—backstays are unheard of—and see that shrouds and forestays are ancient, frayed manila, sometimes rusty wire, but in either case set up to chainplate eyes with ancient, frayed manila lanyards. Often just one rusty bolt, perhaps started, holds a chainplate to a hull. The sails are roped all around, but patched, re-patched, and re-re-patched, apparently as old as the hull itself.

Such are the sails and rigging of the little ships you see off the south coast of St. Thomas, running westward before the Trade, wallowing in big ocean seas with booms broad off and dipping, hulls so heavily laden that amidships both rails may be awash. On that same open coast you see them, not so heavily laden, starting their long beat back against the Trade to Tortola or Virgin Gorda.

If you're in a yacht, you'll overtake and pass such a sloop of equal length, but not as quickly as you at first expect. Running, you may have to break out your spinnaker to overhaul that baggy, long footed, leg o' mutton sail ahead. Beating, you'll go by all right, but you'll find that the old cargo-carrier, with the frayed sheet to her long boom eased and her jib luff sagging, sails about as close to the wind as you do. (She won't sail as close in smooth water, but neither you nor she will often find smooth water in the Caribbean.) An hour or two after you've made, say, Roadtown in Tortola, after a harder beat than you often get at home, the old sloop you passed hours earlier will round the mangroves off Fort Burt and bear off for the public dock. And what, with twenty-four hours in a day, is an hour or two? Or three?

Approaching Roadtown in *Little Dipper* one afternoon, we saw a vicious black squall blowing down on us from Virgin Gorda to the eastward. To avoid narrow waters until the squall had passed, we decided to come about and jog along on the off-shore tack with staysail backed. Our maneuver made—we already had a reef pulled down—we saw a Tortola sloop come out of Roadtown and, a quarter mile to windward of us, stand out for Virgin Gorda on the same offshore tack. The squall enlarged and blotted out the sun, but the old sloop carried all sail right into it. The squall's dark mass blotted her from view and seconds later, with shriek of wind and horizontally driving rain, enveloped us. For some ten minutes *Little Dipper* lay far over, fore-reaching slowly, her weather shrouds bar taut and lee rail under. Able to see nothing, we wondered how that ill-rigged sloop was making out.

Visibility returned. *Little Dipper* regained her feet. Sunshine flooded down, and we saw the squall's dark clouds blowing away to leeward, blotting out the Narrows and the mountains on St. John. But to windward, where the sloop had been, we saw only empty sea.

Then we saw her, far along her course and by now a mile to windward, tiny against horizon islands, sedately sailing and, I guess, hoping for another lift from another blinding, shrieking squall.

There's satisfaction in the thought that a low rig and knowing just what strains rusty wire and frayed manila will endure, serve a *sailor* about as well as bronze and stainless steel.

After doing some carpentry on *Little Dipper* one warm afternoon in March, I emerged from her shed to find the boatyard's slips and buildings shrouded in thick fog. A minute later, as I was walking toward my car, a crack of thunder sounded and a

Niagara of rain poured down. Breaking into a run, I collided with the Major, who was running too. Courses mutually adjusted, we reached the nearest building bow and bow, and paused to catch our breath.

"Notice how fast that came?" he said. "No wind in it, but it might have had wind and taken the rig right out of her!"

Knowing how easily a little ship can be caught over-canvassed by such sneak squalls, he grinned, and the light in his eyes was curiously triumphant. Sharing his sentiment, I grinned back. What both of us had in mind and each was pleased to find the other tuned to is not easy to put into words.

It should be said that service as a lifeboat man along the craggy western coast of Ireland has been part of the Major's vast experience of the sea, as has trawling in those same dangerous waters. Few men have built more little ships that can stand up to the beatings the sea hands out. A boatyard owner now, he makes his living readying yachts for cruising and ocean racing. Here, then, is a man who has spent most of his life combatting the power of wind and sea, yet a man who, when those elements bare their teeth, somehow rejoices.

Something of the same sentiment appears in Conrad. No one has more truly felt it than Slocum, who wrote of the great gale which almost wrecked his ship and drowned him off the Straits of Magellan, "never was the sea more magnificent." Perhaps Belloc has most accurately named this elusive sentiment. Speaking of the damage wrought by gales and other forces of nature, he says that as well as producing fear and sympathy for their victims, these manifestations of nature's power inspire in us a "somber satisfaction."

They do.

Give him a fulcrum, Archimedes said, and he could move the world. One afternoon at my mooring I needed only to move the heel of *Little Dipper*'s mast aft about two inches, but the problem seemed insoluble. Her mast has a massive nine inch section and is about fifty feet long, stepped through the deck. I don't know what that mast must weigh, but once its tongue is in the step and its weight bearing on the step, all looks and feels immovable.

Without giving her the once-over I should have, I'd brought the ship around to her mooring from a winter in the shipyard the day before. Her backstay, I'd noticed, had been slack, and now, aboard to set it up a bit, I'd discovered that the turnbuckle was already taken up all the way. For a while I wondered how a one by nineteen stainless backstay had managed to stretch several inches, and then I remembered that the shipyard had hired a new rigger and that I'd neglected to tell him what the former rigger had known: *Little Dipper*'s mast takes very little rake. Below, at the mast step, I saw what had happened. The rigger had stepped the mast with a normal rake and, aft of the tongue, had driven in a wedge which belonged forward of the tongue. Thus the masthead had been swung many inches aft of the position where her backstay would fit. The rigger had driven in that wedge right smartly, too. Though void of any idea as to how to move the heel of the mast even if I could remove the wedge, I tugged at the wedge with a pair of pliers and of course couldn't budge it.

A friend who worked in a local boatyard came out. He scratched his head and came to the same conclusion I had: neither wedge nor mast was going to budge until the weight of the mast was lifted. Only the shipyard crane could lift that weight.

Two afternoons wasted, I figured. One to sail back up the river to the shipyard and its crane. Another to return. Meanwhile no tuning up, no nothing. Damn.

I phoned the shipyard, got the Major on the wire, and asked when his crane would be available to lift my mast.

"Just stepped your mast," he said.

I described the problem.

"I'll be over and have a look after the whistle blows," he said.

"Bare-handed? It'll take the crane to lift that mast!"

"I'll be over and have a look."

You learn, after a while, not to question the Major's approach to problems of this kind. But this was one problem I felt sure would break his nose. Probably that feeling showed in my face an hour later when his car pulled up to the dock and he got out, bare-handed.

"Let's go!" he said, and his blue eyes snapped defiantly. As we walked down the dock to my dinghy there was a definite swagger in his step. His bare hands looked eager. His military title, I ought to say, derives from an Irish regiment.

We climbed aboard the ship. He glanced at the turnbuckle, shook the backstay, saw that I'd slacked off the forestays, and went below to the mast step.

"See what I mean," I said. "Until the weight of the mast is off the step, we can't move the heel of it aft."

"Got to start that wedge," he muttered.

You sure do, I thought.

He said abruptly, "I have a quarter. Where's your ice pick?"

I saw no connection between the ice pick I handed him and the quarter he dug out of his trousers.

Kneeling, he shoved the point of the ice pick down into the side of the wedge where the wedge just showed its head above the slot in the step that held the mast tongue. He placed the quarter on the oak step and poked the quarter up under the ice pick. Then, the coin giving him a good hard fulcrum under the pick, he bore down on the pick's handle. Slowly, without splitting or shredding, the wedge pried out and tumbled off the step.

"Hmmn," I sighed. "Well, well, well."

"Crane," he muttered. "Oh hell!"

He demanded, "Got a stick of some kind aboard this vessel?

Never go to sea without a stick. I need a stick and a piece of
ιine."

"What kind of stick?"

"Any stick that won't break."

The handle I use in my windlass is the size of a small base-
ball bat. I dug it out and handed it over.

"What kind of line?" I asked.

"Hell—*any* line."

I gave him a fathom or two of worn manila.

He passed one end of the manila around the mast and tied a
bight that loosely encircled the mast. Then, sitting on the cabin
sole and facing the mast with the stick between his legs, he
braced one end of the stick against the mast step and pulled the
loose bight over the stick and about halfway down it. In an
oarsman's posture, he braced his heels against the step, gripped
the upper end of the stick in both hands, and squared his
shoulders. He grunted, pulled back hard against his lever—and
the heel of the mast came aft, snug into its rightful place.

I sighed again, profoundly.

He dropped his tools and stood up.

"You can doubtless tap that wedge in forr'ard of the mast
yourself," he said. His eyes danced, and he added, "Unless your
hammer's out of order."

"If it is," I meekly said, "I'll phone you."


Northerners usually expect to see nature at her most savage
in the tropics, but to me, so far, her tropic guise has been the
peacefulest.

It's true that as I lay becalmed one bright morning in the
Gulf Stream off Bimini and was lounging on my deck, gazing
down into the transparent water, an eight foot shark, brown on
top and livid white below, swam up out of nowhere and, half
rolling over to fix a wicked eye on me, glided past within a few
feet of my face. But skin diving in southern waters has left an

impression stronger still, an impression of how peacefully the different kinds of fish that cluster around reefs and ledges co-exist. Most of these fish, admittedly, dine on plants and crusta-ceans rather than each other, but far down where the light begins to fail you'll sometimes see the shapes of giant grouper, who'll eat anything, including you. And often, just a few feet off your reef, you'll see long blue slim-bodied barracuda, deadly-looking as flat trajectory shells, hanging motionless in the water, eyeing you most steadily. But there the barracuda hang, lazily fanning their pectoral fins, while angel fish, parrot fish, and others seem to go about their occasions with no concern at all for these grim-jawed pirates. In some crevice you may glimpse the dog-like snout of a moray eel, but he too, though his bite is poisonous, appears to trouble no one who does not trouble him.

True, when some large fish swims by, the smaller ones pru-dently give way, often undulating in a body like a flock of birds, but unhurriedly, unanxiously. Surely the big fish along these reefs take occasional small ones, but perhaps they take them so swiftly and discreetly that only the individual prey itself discov-ers what has happened. The ever-present possibility seems not to haunt the others nor darken their cheery lives.

Entirely different was the impression I received one midnight in the Gulf of Maine. The breeze was light, the sea smooth, and I had just hove *Little Dipper* to and was about to go below when, from somewhere off in the night, came a sound of splash-ing. The sound grew louder and came closer, and now was punc-tuated by the slap of eager tails against calm water and by the still louder splashes of leaping fish falling back against the surface. In no time this splashing was all around the ship. A flashlight played across the water revealed no more than swirls and eddies, here and there a flash of silver, but it was obvious that some kind of big fish, probably blues or mackerel, had got into a school of bait. Next came terns and gulls, crying hungrily and diving for the victims' shreds, and soon I heard the pounding of mighty flukes, hard snorts and blowings, the sound of porpoises' bow waves rushing through the dark. Either the school of bait was enormous or the bigger fish, blues or mackerel eating and being eaten, porpoises eating all, were driving it round and round to hold it as cowhands hold excited cattle. The splashing, slapping, rushing, crying, diving continued for an hour. Loons came last, and this midnight carnage rose to its crescendo beneath loons' eerie laughter. In the morning many sharks were visible, their fins weaving back and forth above a once more tranquil sea.

All that savagery took place not far off the staid old town of Portsmouth, New Hampshire.

Belloc wisely advises anyone sighting a sea serpent to keep the fact to himself and thus preserve whatever reputation for veracity he may possess. Not yet having sighted a sea serpent, I haven't had to make the heroic effort prescribed. But for several years I've prudently avoided mention of a most unlikely visitor who came aboard *Little Dipper* at high noon one brilliant summer day when we were halfway from Block Island to Watch Hill. I mention the visitation now, because a friend recently told me of a similar one off the New Jersey coast, which may indicate they're not too rare to be believed. I was at the wheel and my son was sitting in the cockpit, when he suddenly nodded astern and said, "Dad—look!"

What appeared to be a low flying bird was rapidly overtaking us. He skimmed along our wake, rose just high enough to clear our transom, and without ado plumped down on the counter. He lay there on his stomach, breathing heavily. In a moment we saw that he had little leathery ears and, instead of feathers, fur. He was a bat.

Now what business has a bat five or six miles from land at high noon of a brilliant summer day?

While straining credulity I may as well speak of the tiny

birds with gray-brown backs and yellow breasts (warblers?) who came aboard one morning when *Little Dipper* was sailing a smooth sea somewhere east of the Isles of Shoals. Two of these tiny birds appeared together, and were followed by a third. At first I thought them exhausted stragglers from some migration, but the lively way they bounced about the foredeck argued otherwise.

One of them flew astern and made a protracted effort to ride the log line, whose revolutions forced him to scramble like a lumberjack on a rolling log. Disgusted finally at the ways of log lines, he rejoined his fellows on the foredeck, and eventually all three found the starboard railcap the best perch for their purpose, which was earnest and utilitarian: catching gnats. Facing outboard, they rode the railcap for half an hour, from time to time shooting two or three feet into the air where, with audible clicks of beak, they caught their almost invisible prey. Ordinary flies were fair game too, but instead of taking these with wing shots, so to speak, my tiny visitors stalked and took them on the deck, approaching stealthily, injunning forward with bodies low and heads thrust forward for a sudden lightning stab. They rarely missed.

As time went by and their hunger was assuaged, they hopped all over the cabin house and dinghy and finally into the cockpit, where I sat steering. At first I refrained from moving, thinking I might scare them, but after one had perched on my foot and another had got round behind me to where he was in danger of being crushed between my back and the cockpit coaming, I saw my fears were groundless.

Reaching out for one of them, I easily caught him at the first attempt. His indignation was extreme, and he squirmed and wriggled loose. But then, instead of flying off as I'd expected, he stayed well within my reach on the cockpit floor and only shook his head, ruffled his feathers, and eyed me with deep

*Virgin Island News Bureau*

Charlotte Amalie Harbor, St. Thomas

contempt. In fact, he seemed to be a she, because the expression clearly said, "Oaf, you've mussed my dress!"

In a few minutes I oafishly caught another, who was equally indignant but whom I managed to hold onto while I went below and found my camera. Back in the cockpit once more, I snapped his picture with one hand as I held him in the other.

Like good photos generally (aboard *Little Dipper*), this one turned out a perfect blank.

If I could chose between my favorite ten or fifteen anchorages and name one as The Best, I'd likely keep the information to myself. For one of the charms of the spot I'd have in mind, whether a quiet pool among Maine islands or a lee under a bright West Indian beach—maybe one of those open lees you leave on a Trade Wind morning by weighing anchor and simply blowing away to leeward under bare pole while you eat your breakfast—one of the charms, I say, would be privacy. If a favorite cove, lee, or eelrut must be shared, let it be shared with someone who has proved by finding it and working into it on his own that he really likes the place.

Ports, on the other hand, are public. The more boats and sailors in them, the more they offer. I name my favorite port without much hesitation: Charlotte Amalie, St. Thomas.

Perhaps I'm prejudiced, for in that part I met my wife—capsized her, in fact, out of a sailing dinghy on our first date—and in the charter boats moored off the Yacht Haven we have many friends. Not least among these a skipper, best unnamed, who on our arrival from Bermuda one hot evening in July rolled out of his bunk and with a fine disdain for Customs regulations drove me to the ice house so we could build the kind of drinks such an arrival deserves. But there are other reasons, and chief among them is variety of ships and sailors.

One starry night in Charlotte Amalie I watched a big old cargo sloop ghost past my stern. *Little Dipper* and the boats around her lay as still as the dark mountains around the harbor, and the cargo sloop was barely moving. Her huge mainsail hung in a bag, its loose foot trailing overside, and one crewman patiently worked an oar amidships while another tried to tease some air into her jib. Her deck piled high with barrels and lumber, she glided slowly past, headed for a dock where the lights of a modern steamer blazed. Where was the old sloop from, I wondered, and did her crew speak English, French, or Spanish? As she went by it was too dark to read the letters painted on her transom, but her possible home ports were legion and each one had its special character—Grenada, Martinique, St. Bart's, Nevis, Virgin Gorda, Port au Prince, Cap Haitien, Ciudad Trujillo. Everywhere in the Caribbean you'll find sunshine and a sailing breeze, but there the sameness ends and variety takes over. Sooner or later most of that variety passes through Charlotte Amalie.

Another time I watched an ancient plumb-stemmed British yawl tack in, her crew in ragged shorts and bearded, dark with sunburn. The yellow quarantine flag was flying at her spreader, and the home port shown on a life ring at her rail was Durban, South Africa.

Few ocean voyagers miss St. Thomas. My wife was on the dock when Hannes Lindemann paddled up in his canoe.

Then there was the yawl-rigged Bay of Biscay tunnyman off whom I bought a suit of French foul weather gear. She measured seventy feet on deck and had a twenty-two foot beam. Her bow came out of the water like a cliff. Her bulwarks looked as though they'd stop cannonballs. Her main gaff scared me just to see it; the blocks on it were big as pumpkins. Her French owner had sailed her over from France with his wife and baby aboard, and with one veteran Biscayman to help him seemed confident the ship would get them round the world. She looked like she'd shunt ice, but no more go to weather than a coal barge. I asked him if he counted on his engine to keep him off lee shores. Not at all, he told me. Such ships ordinarily had no engines and fished the stormy Bay of Biscay with no navigational equpiment beyond a compass. They made their landfalls anywhere and consequently had to be able to claw off any shore in any weather. A Force Seven wind, he added with a smile, was not much more than a summer breeze to her.

It's in Charlotte Amalie, too, that you'll see Jack Carstarphen sailing his forty foot *Shellback* into her slip with a load of tourists aboard. His wife, Ruth, serves as crew, and between them they handle *Shellback* like a motor scooter. Or you'll see Dick Griffin coming in from longer charters in his husky gaff-rigged cutter *Quandy*. As he shoots for the dock and goes forward to his halyards you expect his main to drop, but it does not. Instead, he heaves on a line that brails the sail to mast and gaff. One heave and the main's secured. No flogging, no easing a boom into a gallows, no furling, no fuss. Dick has no boom to try his soul as your boom so often does try yours, especially if you cruise offshore. The heart of this rig is a vang that controls the gaff. John Alden designed the rig for ocean sailing. It has a lot to recommend it.

Come winter the *Danmark*, a full rigged Danish training ship, seldom fails to call at this old Danish port. Her officers know how to sail her. I've seen them sail her anchor out and beat out of the harbor under sail alone, all lowers drawing and upper topsails breaking out.

In Charlotte Amalie you'll see a greater variety of ships and perhaps a saltier brand of sailor than in any other port in occidental waters. And you see them in a harbor circled by green mountains, mountains that shut out the wild Atlantic and stand away to the westward in sunlit peaks that brush the Trade Wind's clouds.

To my mind the most dangerous waters likely to be visited by cruising boats along the Atlantic coast are those that wash the great capes of the Carolinas—Cape Fear, Cape Lookout, and terrible Cape Hatteras. Unless he motors along the Intracoastal Waterway, which soon grows tedious at the slow speeds auxiliary engines make, a northern sailor bound for Florida or the

*Bob Simpson*

Schooner *Tontine* southwest of Hatteras. She left Nassau a month before *Little Dipper*

Bahamas or returning from them must weather these great capes. At first glance, perhaps, though harbors hereabouts are sixty to one hundred miles apart, the dangers aren't apparent. These capes are lighted, and the winds that sweep them are probably no stronger than winds elsewhere. But there's more to these capes than this.

From all of them sandy shoals make out a long way into the open ocean. From Cape Fear shoals make out no less than thirty-five miles. On parts of these shoals a small boat will ground even in a quiet sea, and in any weight of wind or sea huge breakers build up all along them. Further, these capes are not headlands like Cape Elizabeth, Maine, or Montauk Point, Long Island. They are sandy, horizon-hugging beaches, invisi- ble a few miles off, and the mainland back of them is low salt marsh. Reaching along a coast like this before a nor'wester in the fall or a sou'wester in the spring, even a skipper watchful for steepening seas might, especially at night or in rain, find his ship caught up and hurled by breakers before he had any suspicion breakers were at hand.

You say a competent skipper should know at all times where he is? That's often impossible along this coast, and the impos- sibility of it is the chief cause of the myriad wrecks that dot the coastal charts. The main axis of the Gulf Stream swings past not far offshore, and the Stream's strong currents, notoriously vari- able, complicate even a coaster's reckoning. They cause large errors in the DR figured from the last fix got by a skipper who's well out in the Stream.

We had a taste of this in June of '61 when for two consecu- tive days as we rode the Stream northward from the Straits of Florida and reckoned on a two knot northward drift, our noon fixes showed we'd overrun our DR by forty miles one day, forty- five the other. Welcome news, but sobering. And still this isn't all.

Not only are you likely to be unsure of your position when you angle out of the Stream and head in toward some Carolina port, but you're likely to encounter the deceptive haze which we encountered on the trip above. To close the coast from a known position, we angled out of the Stream and made for the lighted bell moored in deep water some twenty miles off Cape

Romain. We picked it up one evening and, free of Gulf Stream current, took a departure northward for the coast just west of the Cape Fear River entrance, about seventy miles away.

Next day found us running before a strong sou'wester under a bright blue sky. Toward noon the mileage on the log put us within six miles of land, but as the ship went rolling on before big seas at better than six knots no land appeared. I got the sextant out, caught noon, and went below to work the sight. Plotting it on the coastal chart, I found myself drawing a position line that lay *inland* of the coast, except in a shallow bight just west of Cape Fear River. In that bight my line was nowhere more than three miles off the beach.

At that moment Lucy called from the wheel, "Land right ahead!"

Land was no more than two or three miles away, devilishly low and blurred by a haze which a bright sky and clear horizon had given us no reason to suspect.

Of the three great capes, Hatteras is notoriously the worst. Not only is it the lowest of them all, a strip of sand and nothing more, but it's cut off from the mainland back of it by the whole width of Pamlico Sound. Off Hatteras the mainland can't be seen. And at Hatteras the Gulf Stream swings in across the shoals.

A small boat rounding Hatteras surely ought to give that cape a berth of a hundred miles. Indeed, remembering how unpredictable the North Atlantic is, and that both Slocum and Robinson met heavy longlasting gales off the Atlantic coast in June, I'd say that a small boat rounding Hatteras ought to round it via Bermuda.

But to me the question's academic. Coasting home from Florida I won't go round Hatteras at all. I'll do what I did in '61: put in at Morehead City on Cape Lookout, run the ten mile cut north to the Neuse River, and then sail down the

Neuse and across Pamlico Sound to Oregon Inlet, safely north of Hatteras and its shoals. This sneak through sheltered waters pleasantly varies an ocean cruise. Oregon Inlet's buoyed and lighted, easy to leave or enter in good weather.

# CHAPTER IX

## *Cruising Gear and Wrinkles*

Many beginners jump right into racing. I was one of them. One summer I was alarmed to find myself aboard a vehicle which had no brakes, and the next summer I was timing starts with a stopwatch and trying for (if seldom getting) the safe leeward position. And the jump from there to a berth on an ocean racer, where someone else makes the decisions, pilots and navigates the ship, checks and maintains her gear, is often not a great one. Many a beginner steers that course and comes to equate seamanship with skill at racing.

Racing is great fun, and the man who never races his boat never learns to get out of her what designer, builder, and sailmaker have put in. And yet, somewhere this side of the specialized art of winning races lies all the basic seamanship which enabled Joshua Slocum to cruise around the world alone.

Cruising puts such premium on ground tackle that I've found you can judge a man's cruising experience pretty accurately by looking at the kind and condition of the ground tackle aboard his boat. The further he has cruised and the more bottoms he has dug his hook into, the better planned and usually the heavier his ground tackle will be.

Three anchors, each with its own rode of at least thirty-five fathoms seem to me essential on a cruising boat. More than once I have put two anchors down and then had a shift of wind which, but for a third anchor, would have put me ashore or on a ledge. In '55 the warnings for Hurricane Edna found me in a crowded harbor which offered no room to swing. Lacking a fourth anchor, I had to string a line halfway across the harbor to a bollard on a dock.

There's much to be said for modern lightweight anchors. Properly dug in, they develop enormous holding power. But I think there's this to be said against them: to get them properly dug in often requires more scope or in gusty weather more time than you can give. I like an anchor that takes hold on short scope and takes hold NOW. Consequently *Little Dipper*'s bower is a forty pound Herreshoff. As supplement for this or for anchoring in a tideway where the current will reverse its direction, *Little Dipper* carries a thirty pound CQR, an anchor which cannot foul its rode. Both Carol (unannounced) and Edna caught me off cruising, but these two anchors, each with two fathoms of chain on it and thirty-five fathoms of manila rode paid out, took the worst of both hurricanes without dragging.

My third anchor was chosen with the above mentioned wind shift in mind. When that shift threatens to upset a satisfactory situation you may not have much room to pay out scope in the new direction. *Little Dipper*'s Sitting Bull is a sixty pound Herreshoff. Maybe it should be heavier.

Ground tackle can hold no longer than the fitting to which you make it fast. A rode's bitter end should always be bent around the mast, but you hope the mast won't have to hold her. A sampson post or bitts built into the keel seem to me essential, and on a ship more than, say, twenty-five feet over all I'd call a windlass essential, too. A cleat, even if bolted through the deck, seems no answer at all. A windlass will often be needed to break out an anchor, and bitts built into the keel will hold on long after deck planks and a cleat bolted through them have carried away.

Several years ago a thunderstorm taught me that I had never learned the right way of making a rode fast to post or windlass. Instead of the short blow I expected, this thunderstorm (accompanied by a waterspout) blew with hurricane force for nearly an hour. It built up an altogether unexpected sea in the river in which I lay, and the ship began dragging. I clawed my way forward to pay out more scope—and discovered that scope couldn't be paid out. I had put a clove hitch around one barrel of my windlass and, to secure this hitch, another one around the other barrel. The rode was secure, but to pay out scope I would have had to cast off the hitches, and with the wind then blowing the rode would have snaked out uncontrollably. Only the bend around the mast would have stopped it. Luckily, I had anchored where there was room and time to put down a second anchor.

To make a rode secure is not enough. You must be able to pay out scope in all conditions. Since that thunderstorm I have taken three turns around the barrel of my windlass and then secured the rode with a steamboat hitch around the standing part. A steamboat hitch cannot jam, as a clove hitch will when wet. It is secure, which one clove hitch never is. And when I cast off my steamboat hitch I still have those three turns around the windlass, and they allow me to control the rode and pay out scope as I please. (With a cleat, this kind of control is difficult or impossible.)

There's a lot of virtue in a round turn. At least one should be taken wherever possible: around bollards, around anything to be lashed on deck. As for the clove hitch, I've come to lump it with watch charm anchors and bow cleats as evidence of inexperience. I think its only place for any purpose is around a line's standing part, after turns have been taken.

A device that's useful both in crowded harbors and in open roadsteads is a weight slung on the rode and lowered halfway down to the anchor. Take a pig of lead (or a deep sea sounding lead), bore a hole in one end, and strap on a big shackle. Now you can shackle this weight to your rode and, using a light line bent to the shackle, lower the weight down the rode. Working as a spring against the pitching of your boat, this weight has the effect of greatly increasing your scope. Looked at another way, you might say it enables you to put down a much heavier anchor and raise it in two easy stages. If your shackle is big, nothing can foul and the weight comes up easily. Its convenience depends on rigging it before the season starts and keeping it handy.

Seeing people throw an anchor over and wait for the boat to fall back and dig it in gives me the willies. I like to lower my anchor to the bottom, not throw it, and feel it touch, turn over, and take hold right. Scope can be paid out afterward. Then I know the fluke is into the bottom, and if a breeze wakes me up at midnight I can yawn and roll over, confident the anchor will hold.

It should be a rule on all boats that regardless of who has put the anchor down and made the rode fast, the owner comes forward and checks the whole job, thereby taking responsibility for it. If you crew for an owner foolish enough to neglect this, remind him of it. He knows his gear better than you do, and his boat should be on his conscience, not yours.

A piece of seamanship not seen as often aboard *Little Dipper* as it should be is taking soundings before putting an anchor down. Several times within the past year I've anchored in water deeper than expected, which means paying out much more scope and leads to more work getting the anchor up. There's no trick to using the lead as you slowly luff up to an anchorage, though it's a good idea to secure the end of the line.

Hurricanes have taught us that along the Atlantic and Gulf coasts the wind can blow as hard as it blows in the Southern Ocean. But if you're planning a first cruise offshore, another fact should enter your calculations: a small boat is troubled more by seas than by the wind. True, the ordinary long ocean sea affects a small boat less than a big one, but in strong winds these long ocean seas develop a good deal of cross-chop on top. Offshore you generally find two wave systems moving through the same water in different directions, and even in summer you can count on being tossed about much more than in coastwise cruising, where the seas usually run with the wind.

With this rougher motion in mind, it seems to me that running backstays should be fitted on any boat going offshore. Adding runners to a boat which now needs only a shift of the helm to come about may at first glance seem merely to increase the work. But once you are offshore with the seas trying to throw your mast overside, your second and third glances at a strong pair of runners will vastly comfort you. You'll be a long way from a harbor or a shipyard, and if your permanent backstay goes, you still have those runners, or vice versa.

For the same reasons it seems to me that a vessel cruising offshore requires two forestays. Here is the chief virtue, I'd say, of the double head rig, which admittedly can be a nuisance when short tacking inshore. A sloop rig will give almost the same insurance if a second forestay is fitted alongside the first. Once that second forestay has been fitted, you'll know that one fatigued or faulty turnbuckle cannot dump the whole rig on your head.

No one seems to know what to do about metal fatigue. Stainless steel wire, for example, looks as good when ready to part as when it's new, a fact which has made some deep water men favor galvanized rigging. The best answer to the problem, in tangs and turnbuckles as well as wire, seems to be to plan the rig in such a way that if something parts, something else will keep the mast in the boat.

The double head rig scores again, I think, because it ordinarily includes a masthead jib. This gives you an additional halyard to the masthead, handy for going aloft and a stand-by if the main halyard parts.

*Little Dipper*'s running backstays and two headsails, both loose footed, give a crew many lines to tend when coming about. Racing, the crew earns its keep. But in cruising all these lines need not be tended at once. Runners can be left slack in coming about and set up later. When singlehanding and short tacking in strong winds, you can trim the staysail amidships, which serves for both tacks, or you can let it come aback on one tack. Why knock yourself out?

Navigators and skippers of crack ocean racers view taffrail logs with some disfavor, as drags on speed. That's figuring things pretty fine. The rest of us, especially when cruising shorthanded and too busy to maintain a constant check of our position, do well to stream a log. When the wind is free and steady, a man who knows his ship can accurately estimate his speed and distance run, but over an average day the wind varies a good deal. It's a great help to be able to turn the problem over to a log and forget about it, knowing that at any moment, regardless of variations in speed, you have an accurate record of distance run.

Granted a free wind and a log, sailing in fog is usually no great problem. Steering carefully and going from buoy to buoy, you'll usually pick up your marks as planned, though if your mark is a horn or whistle it pays to remember that while sound carries a long way downwind, it goes upwind hardly at all. Lay a course that will bring you to leeward of such a mark. Once you hear it, you can work up to it for your next departure.

A variation of that principle is useful when closing a shore after running some distance without any check of position. Hold well above the place you want to make on that shore, and then, when you see or hear the shore, you know you're above your destination and need only run down to it. If you steer directly for your destination and miss it, you probably won't know whether you're high or low of it.

Keeping these wrinkles in mind when fog comes in, you can usually arrange to give yourself, not a small and difficult target, but a general target area you can't easily miss.

Tacking is a fogrunner's real problem. Here you have not only to figure the distance run on each tack but the course actually steered, which isn't easy in a wind that alternately lets you up and heads you. I carry pencil and paper in my shirt pocket for such occasions and try to record changes in the course, as well as any bearings or other information that may turn up. But tacking in a fog, particularly when current is involved, is a blind proposition at best. Here, too, your best hope lies in having worked out a large area free of dangers to aim at.

While it's well to figure currents, course steered, leeway, and distance run as closely as you can, it's even better to view the results of such figuring with constant scepticism. That may somewhat discourage elaborate reckoning—I'm afraid it does aboard *Little Dipper*—but a sceptic will keep his lead going, his eyes and ears open, and is not likely to get into trouble. The man who knows just where he is because his slide rule told him so is the one most likely to pile up.

When you do miss a mark in fog, your situation may permit you to "sail a square"—say a half mile east, a mile north, a mile west, a mile south, and finally another half mile east, back to where you started (maybe). If this fails to locate the mark, you'd better heave to on the offshore tack, or anchor. If the depth is too great to anchor, pay out your rode anyway and let your anchor hang. It will take hold if you drift into shoal water.

To my mind no one should cruise offshore without a strong boom gallows which has thwartships bracing. For coastwise cruising a boom crutch may suffice. It can be set up in the smooth water of a harbor. At sea, trying to guide a heavy boom into a slender crutch is a job for someone who has doubled his accident insurance. Further, once you've got the boom in the gallows and the mainsail is being repaired or a trysail being bent on, the gallows must be strong enough to take the weight of the crew, who will be hanging onto the boom in a seaway and will often be thrown hard against it. Many gallows are little more than booby traps. If a gallow does carry away, broken arms and legs may result. All this holds equally for calms at sea, where the roll may be severe.

Ocean racers seem to get along without downhauls on their sails (though many might have used downhauls in the 1960 Bermuda Race), but anyone who cruises shorthanded will find downhauls a tremendous help. Rigging a downhaul is simple: strap a pulley near the tack of the sail; when the sail is furled bend a line to its halyard shackle, reeve this line through the pulley, and bring the coil aft. As you hoist the sail, the line pays out through the pulley, and when the sail is fully hoisted you secure the fall somewhere near the mast. When you want to take in the sail and have slacked off the halyard, heave on this downhaul. It will bring the luff all the way down and clamp it against the pulley. No going out on the bowsprit or even to the bow. No tugging at a flogging sail that doesn't want to come in or gets away from you and starts back up. With your downhaul on it, that sail *has* to come in. The downhaul does give you another line to manage in addition to the halyard, but both can be managed by one man near the mast. Downhauls may seem extra work in light airs, but they prove wonderful labor savers and wetting preventers in heavy weather. *Little Dipper* has a downhaul on her jib at all times.

One contraption you'll never find on any ship of mine is a reel winch. Bluntly, I wouldn't give a reel winch hellroom. For one thing this type of winch takes forever to get a sail up a mast or forestay, and there are times when you want to make sail fast. Nothing looks more lubberly than a sail flogging itself to death while a perfectly healthy man slowly cranks it up a mast with a hundred dollar winch. But this is nothing compared to the injuries these expensive gadgets cause. Hardly a summer goes by without word that someone has had a hand or an arm broken or his physiognomy re-arranged when one of these winches unexpectedly slipped its catch and fanned him with its metal handle.

If you must have wire halyards, splice rope tails into them and use rope winches which turn one way only. Better yet, since rope-into-wire splices eventually need renewing and may need it some windy night at sea, use the system Gil Dunham used on his sloop *Pooh-Bah*. Instead of splicing tails to his wire halyards, he tucked eye splices into the wire, around thimbles, and spliced the tails into these eyes. Each eye was made at such a point that when the sail was fully hoisted the eye was only an inch or two off the barrel of the winch. Halyards made up this way give you the straight luffs which only wire can give, have all the handiness of rope halyards, and their tails are easy to renew.

It's curious how many owners (and builders) fit their boats with refrigerators, gimballed tables, ship-to-shore radios, fathometers, and other costly gadgets without getting around to the simple things that add much more to comfort and safety.

You don't have to cross an ocean to want occasionally to go below and sleep while underway, but in any sort of sea the bunk your builder provides leaves much to be desired. It's likely to be so wide that even when you've made bunk boards to prevent falling out of it you roll to port and starboard every time the boat rolls. Wide bunks are well enough in harbors, impossible at sea. *Little Dipper* owes her bunk scheme to Dwight McVitty, who worked it out before we sailed south in '55, and it not only chocks the sleeper in, preventing roll, but has the added virtue of simplifying making beds. Figured for *Little Dipper*'s cabin, where the outboard sides of the bunks butt against unencumbered outward curves of ceiling, the system might not suit all boats, but seems worth describing.

Instead of bunk boards McVitty worked up semi-hammocks. They're rectangular pieces of canvas, six feet long and about two feet wider than the bunks, with half a dozen grommets along each side. One of these sides is hooked into a horizontal row of hooks in the ceiling about a foot higher than the bunk, and then the canvas is laid across the bunk so that its inboard side overhangs the inboard side of the bunk. Mattress and bedding are laid on the canvas, and two or three lanyards are tied to the grommets in the canvas's inboard side. These lanyards go to pad-eyes in the carlins overhead and, when set up, hold up the inboard side of the canvas so that it acts much like a bunk board. The sleeper's weight rests on the bunk, but the canvas fits him snugly and chocks him in, as a bunk board doesn't.

When a watch below is over, you make up these bunks by simply lifting the inboard side of the canvas to another and higher row of hooks along the ceiling. With this one move your bed's made, your bedding's out of the way, and the bunk along the side of the cabin has a nice soft back rest.

Everyone who's cruised at all has been thrown about below with real danger of breaking an arm or leg. Few builders provide effective handholds. On *Little Dipper* we've bolted brass hand grips to the sides of the cabin at shoulder level, two to port and two to starboard. On a wider vessel these might be supplemented by an overhead grab rail fastened to the carlins the length of the cabin.

Cooking in a seaway is never easy. The cook deserves all help possible. One of the best helps is a strap whose ends are made fast to the galley, about hip high, with hooks and eyes. Working like a window washer's strap, this strap holds the cook in place regardless of the boat's heel. Once hooked in, he can use both hands to rustle up your dinner.

No little ship should leave her mooring without a safety belt aboard for every member of the crew. A safety belt is merely a canvas strap which buckles around the chest (not the stomach), has shoulder straps to keep it up, and has spliced onto it a length of line with a snaphook at the end. This snaphook can be clapped to the rigging anywhere, and it makes the man in the belt fast to the ship. You don't have to fall overboard to discover the value of a safety belt. It breeds confidence when you're working forward, maybe with green water coming over, and it lets you work with both hands. It's reassuring when you're alone on deck at night and find yourself dozing off. You soon get used to wearing it. I wear mine regularly when singlehanding, and my wife and I wear them at all times offshore and at night.

Granted safety belts, it seems to me that on a smallish boat rigid lifelines on metal stanchions become unnecessary. Not only are these lifelines expensive, but often they're so low that they trip you rather than support you. You can always fall over them and probably through them. You can't fall out of a safety belt. This simple piece of gear which anyone can make is the greatest safety factor ever introduced in small boat sailing.

The author showing life line rig

# CHAPTER X

## *Seamanship in Heavy Weather*

Most of us are better sailors in light weather than in heavy. This not only because light weather makes everything easy and does not punish mistakes, but because in summer when we do most of our sailing heavy weather is uncommon. We lack experience of it. As a result when the wind does pipe up in summertime many skippers find themselves crashing through rough water under far more sail than they can really manage. Wind and ship take charge, and skipper and crew hang on, hoping the rig will bear it and that she'll answer to her rudder well enough to make a harbor.

That's no way to enjoy cruising. Its strain on men and gear can be avoided by making the most of heavy weather when it comes. Although he had in mind a professional master aboard an unfamiliar ship, Captain Voss laid down a rule every amateur should heed: "It is the duty of every shipmaster to make trials . . . at the beginning of the first gale he encounters." An hour or two of trial and experiment in a blow, "operating" your ship, as Voss calls it, will build up more confidence and know-how than a dozen blows which you merely survive.

I remember my surprise when I first experimented with heaving to. I was singlehanded and running down from Casco Bay in a strong norther which had covered the sea with white caps. The wind was pressing against my neck and humming in the rigging. *Little Dipper* seemed under control, but she was yawing a bit and I had begun to wonder what would happen if the wind blew much harder. You know the feeling.

Having read about heaving to, I decided to try it. The staysail wasn't drawing, and it was easy to pull it to weather with the windward sheet. I trimmed the main and slowly brought the ship toward the wind. As the wind came abeam the ship heeled over and her speed, now added to the wind's, increased the general hurlyburly and sense of strain. As I brought her on the wind, she took a couple of dives into the seas, and then the backed staysail slowed her and the diving stopped. I kept her on the wind with the rudder, the main helped to keep her there, and soon she was riding the seas like a duck, easily and comfortably, in a wind that seemed to have lightened by half. After experimenting with the helm and mainsheet, I found the trim she liked and discovered that I could lash the helm and wander about the deck or go below and stay there. She lay steadily, about four points off the wind, with the main holding her up and the backed staysail preventing her from moving forward or coming about. She kept a steady heel, and as the seas rolled under her she pitched only slowly. All sense of strain had gone. Below, her motion was barely noticeable.

The episode was an eye-opener and wonderfully reassuring. My ship did, after all, have brakes.

Since then I have hove to for many reasons besides easing the ship in heavy weather: to cook and eat in comfort, to reef when singlehanding, to take soundings, chart courses, sleep. Often it's just a matter of pulling a headsail a-weather.

Every ship has her own ways of heaving to. These depend on her rig, underwater profile, and the condition of wind and sea. With *Little Dipper* in fresh conditions, simply pulling the staysail a-weather and adjusting the main comes close to stopping her (though if both headsails are hoisted the jib may have to come in). If the main tends to flog when the sheet is started, easing the halyard a few inches transforms the flog into a slow flap. When reefing singlehanded I trim her this way, except maybe not pulling the staysail all the way to weather, because the main must be lowered about a third of its hoist. When the main is down that far, I bring in the boom with the sheet, and reef at leisure. She lies there at a steady heel, moving slowly. Under such conditions reefing singlehanded is not hard labor.

My ship also heaves to without her main. Pull her staysail somewhat a-weather, put her helm down, and she'll lie about five points off the wind, forereaching slowly if the wind is strong.

As well as different ways of heaving to, depending on the ship, her rig, and the state of the sea, there are different degrees of heaving to. With the headsail backed, the main will still drive her forward at reduced speed, and to stop her completely you may have to put considerable luff in the main. If so and the sea is rough, you prevent the boom from jumping with your boom-guy—which for this or any other purpose can be most readily trimmed if you reeve it through a snatch block at the bow and bring the fall aft to a cleat near the cockpit.

Once stopped, a boat will drift to leeward, and you may want to keep her moving ahead just enough to compensate for this drift. Adjustment of sails and helm provides the answer. Again, as happened to me in a norther off Hispaniola, you may want to keep sailing to windward as much as possible while you sleep. For this, on my ship in strong winds and big seas, you pull the staysail perhaps half a-weather and haul the main pretty close. Trimmed that way she lacks both the speed and the inclination to come about, but she'll sail herself, closer to the wind than ever, and will make a steady two knots. Slow? Sure, but it was mighty nice to come up from below after seven hours' sleep and discover that she had logged fifteen miles on a course closer to the wind than I could have sailed her.

I've never tried heaving to in a centerboarder and don't know if they'll heave to properly. With the board up, obviously, they have little grip on the water and fly off to leeward like balloons. When the board is down, I've been told, it bangs back and forth, trying to tear the trunk out. Other people tell me that centerboards designed and built to fit their trunks snugly do not have this failing. Whatever the verdict on centerboarders, the ability to heave to is one of the most useful a cruising boat can have. I'd call it utterly essential when you're shorthanded, as you usually are when cruising.

Few things add as much to a boat's comfort and the happiness of her crew as the ability to pull down a reef quickly and easily. Roller reefing seems the answer to many, but roller reefing is expensive and it brings aboard one more gadget that may get out of whack. I've used the fisherman method of reefing for years, and I doubt that roller reefing can be much easier.

My mainsail has two rows of reef points sewn in the sail, one row cotton and the other manila to prevent confusing them at night. Starting off on a cruise, I reeve both the tack and clew pendants when the sail is hoisted and thereafter carry them rove and ready to use. The tack pendant is rove through its cringle in the luff and down around the gooseneck, where the ends tie together. To reeve the clew pendant I tied a stopper knot in one end, then pass the other end through a B block on one side of the boom, up through the cringle, down through a corresponding block on the other side of the boom, then forward along the underside of the boom to a cleat near the gooseneck. With this rig, when I have a crew and want to reef, one man goes forward, slacks off the halyard (after setting up the topping lift), pulls down the tack pendant and makes it fast. He finds the clew pendant right beside him, heaves on it, belays it to the cleat, and the reef is as good as in. The points can be tied at leisure.

With the pendants rove in advance there are no points or pendants (except for the second reef) to bring up from below, where they often get mislaid, and no acrobatics out on the counter trying to snare a flapping cringle. The helmsman controls the boom with the sheet. One other man does the rest. The B blocks, of course, must be carefully positioned on the boom, so that when the clew is pulled down it is also pulled out along the boom. The clew pendant serves both purposes.

Once your reef is in and the sail drawing, it's wise to check the sail from time to time by sighting along the line of reef points. Often the after points, which take the most strain, will be pulled higher off the boom than the forward ones. That does no damage, provided the line of reef points is straight and the clew cringle lies fairly on that line. But if the clew is pulled down unfairly, ease the pendant. Strapping the pendant down harder than the points can result in a rip just when you least want it.

Off the wind, pulling down a reef or sailing under headsail alone makes a boat easier to steer and reduces the chance of broaching. On the wind, reefing the main or partly backing a headsail lengthens out the seas and eases ship and crew. Even the strongest ship will begin to leak and wear out her rigging if she is always driven into head seas at full speed. The sailors in the Bahamas and Caribbean can teach us a lot about seamanship. With rigging and sails that do not look as if they'd hang together in any but the lightest breezes, these seamen make long passages where seas run high and winds blow hard. Anyone can buy a strong boat and drive her to death or an annual re-building. It takes seamanship to judge what strains gear can stand and to know how and when to ease it.

Sails, incidentally, will live longer if you avoid the flogging that occurs when sails are lowered with the ship on or into the wind. Head off a bit while headsails are coming in, and they'll come in without flogging.

The above should not encourage anyone to go to sea in any but the strongest ship he can afford, however small she may be, maintained in top condition. The price of going to sea any other way may be disaster and will certainly be anxiety. You know how it is. Once or twice a summer we run into blows that really test our boats, and suddenly our thinking goes a lot deeper than usual. In NORTH BY EAST Rockwell Kent gives an amusing example. Lying in his bunk off Newfoundland in heavy weather, he reflects, "The keel is an iron casting weighing three tons. It is secured to the boat by vertical iron bolts. On the ends of these bolts are nuts screwed upon slender threads. It is those threads that hold that iron to the boat. God, is that all!"

There are other slender things—shackle pins, the wire in shackle pins, turnbuckles, rudder hangings, the pin through the main halyard sheave—on which everything else may depend. Once or twice a summer we give these things some earnest thought when we can't do much about them. If we have methodically checked them over, some before the boat is launched in the spring, others two or three times a summer, those periods of thought can be reassuring.

Although a North Atlantic gale may not reach the peak strength of a hurricane, such a gale can produce gusts of hurricane force and, worse, keep blowing for days and nights on end. In planning cruises in open water, particularly in the spring or fall, the long duration of gales and the distance a ship hove to may drift should be kept in mind.

Let's set up some figures. Suppose we have a boat which, hove to under storm trysail in a heavy gale, drifts to leeward at a speed of two knots. Many shoal draft boats would drift faster, but let's use two knots. If the gale blew forty-eight hours, our boat will drift ninety-six miles. That means that if she'd been hit by a severe nor'easter while going outside from the Chesapeake around Cape Hatteras, she would have to have been a hundred and twenty miles off that cape to escape breaking up on its outlying shoals. To give her crew any peace of mind, she would have to have been much further off, with sea room for at least another day's drift. And we have figured on only a two day gale and a drift of two knots. Moral: think twice about making the Chesapeake a point of departure for a trip around Hatteras.

There are four well known methods of riding out a storm at sea. One consists of taking in all sail except a tiny mizzen and streaming a sea anchor to keep the ship's head more or less into the wind. Voss proved the practicability of this in *Tilikum*, the sailing canoe in which he crossed three oceans. Thanks largely to Voss—whose VENTURESOME VOYAGES and its Appendix deserve reading by anyone cruising offshore—the sea anchor has saved many lifeboats. On the other hand, most deepwater men doubt a sea anchor's value in a boat much over four or five tons. The strains set up by gale winds and seas and the plunging of the boat would make chafe difficult if not impossible to prevent. It's doubtful that even the strongest sea anchor would hang together for long while holding a boat of ten tons. Moreover, a boat riding by a sea anchor to the bow drifts backward, which puts enormous strains on the rudder.

Another method is to heave to under a storm trysail, stopping the boat or nearly so and letting her drift offwind. I have used this method with *Little Dipper* in a gale that hit seventy-five. Nothing is easy in such a gale and I would suppose that only a large ship could be at all comfortable, but a trysail often steadies a boat and so reduces the misery.

As Eric Hiscock has said, only he who has set a trysail in a gale can have any idea of the danger and difficulty involved. It pays to be forehanded when possible and hoist the trysail soon. In any event, a switch track down the side of the mast on which the trysail is bent and brailed in good weather will greatly facilitate the job.

Before a trysail is hoisted both its sheets should be turned around headsail sheet winches, after being rove through snatch blocks aft, and then made fast to cleats. Taking most of the pull on the windward sheet puts a bag in the sail which prevents forward progress, and this may permit heaving to without a storm jib. The weight, size, and cut of a trysail require careful calculation to fit the particular boat, and here you want the advice of an experienced sailmaker. Further, nothing about the rig can be too strong. Pad-eyes to which snatch blocks for the sheet are fastened should be bolted through deck beams (as should all cleats anyway), and it's good insurance to through-bolt the sail track at the point where it takes the head of the try-sail. *Little Dipper*'s track is also bolted where it takes the head of the main, normally and when reefed.

Suppose the wind blows too hard to carry any sail, or suppose it rips your trysail off. In my ship, which has more forefoot than is usual nowadays and a deep draft, the amount of sea room available would affect my choice of the alternatives re-maining. In the gale mentioned above we drifted to leeward for thirty-six hours at an average speed of a knot and a half. I'm sure this is less drift than would have occurred if we had run off towing warps. Therefore if I could not carry sail and wanted to keep drift to a minimum (and take it easy below), I would lie a-try under bare pole. Experimenting with this method in a moderate gale at sea several years ago, I found that with the helm lashed down *Little Dipper* lay about seven points off the wind. She wasn't as steady as under trysail, but as she drifted off she left a good smooth to windward. On the other hand, on my last trip to the Caribbean I found that she rode more easily ly-ing a-try under bare pole than hove to under trysail. Gale con-ditions vary, and it pays to avoid hard and fast rules. If one method isn't satisfactory, try another.

When a boat lies a-try under a bare pole with her helm lashed down, she'll lie more or less beam to the seas, and a gale wind in her rigging will keep her well heeled and thus increase her freeboard on the windward side. She leaves the smooth made by her drift just where you want it, dead to windward, and in this posture oil bags slung over bow and stern will prove effec-tive. Lying in the trough of gale seas, a steamer might roll her guts out, but a little ship is only lifted up and lowered down. In *Cohoe*, a vessel of deep draft, Adlard Coles lay a-try without damage in a hurricane of long duration.

If dangerous seas begin to break through your windward

smooth and sweep your deck, the only tactic left is to put warps over the stern, up your helm, and scud off before it. The greater the diameter of these warps the more good they will do, and if you lash a spare mainsail to one of them it will do more good still. For as long as it held together a sea anchor would be useful, too, and oil bags could be slung over the bow, giving the oil a chance to spread before it fell too far astern. Scudding off, of course, you must steer, keeping her stern to the big ones, which would soon become an ordeal, especially at night. Slocum used this method in a gale off the Straits of Magellan. Robinson used it in his "ultimate storm" and discusses it in his latest book.

Towing a warp need not be confined to hard chances. A warp towed when running off before any strong wind will reduce the chances of broaching or being pooped. Under such conditions it's a good device if the helmsman is tired or inexperienced.

Tactics for surviving a storm depend on the particular boat and situation, but two principles are worth remembering. First, a boat that's stopped or moving only slowly is much safer than a boat moving at any rate of speed. On the wind, a stopped boat will rise to oncoming seas like a cork instead of diving into them. When off the wind, a boat running slowly does not make bow or quarter waves, and it's usually the quarter waves which lead to pooping by disturbing overtaking seas and causing them to break. Also, when running at very slow speeds a boat's stern lifts easily, again like a cork.

The second principle is to get a smooth to windward. A boat hove to and stopped, drifts offwind, making a smooth on her windward side, and if this smooth can be kept between the boat and oncoming seas it takes most of the poison out of them. As they reach it, it has a wonderful smothering effect on their breaking crests. Scudding off, warps towed astern not only slow you down but exert the same smothering effect.

It should be remembered that heaving to puts great strain on the rudder. A ship does not lie perfectly still, but will now and then range forward and fall back. When she falls back her whole weight comes against the rudder, and the rudder can be damaged by being banged against its stops. The wheel or tiller should be lashed in such position that this can't happen. If a boat falls back too much or too often, it may be wise to let her forereach a little by adjusting sails or helm.

All hands agree that carrying on too long is the commonest cause of damage and disaster in small boats at sea. Beating or reaching, no sane man is likely to carry on too long, for on these points of sailing the angle of heel and seas crashing over the windward rail warn him when his boat is overpowered. Running, these warnings are absent, and a prudent skipper bears in mind that it takes, not a whole ocean dangerously convulsed, but only one bad sea to put him out of business for keeps. Looking port and starboard as he runs, he may see nothing that looks dangerous—"dangerous" can be defined as breaking crests higher than his freeboard—but astern, which direction concerns him most when running, his quarter wave will be to some degree interfering with every sea that comes along. Odd seas much bigger and steeper than those around them do now and then occur, and if one of these odd seas happens to roll up behind him and topple at his quarter wave, he can be stove in or overturned.

A prudent skipper keeps a watchful eye astern. When seas in that direction become noticeably worse than elsewhere, or if steering becomes difficult, it's time to slow down or stop. Allowance should also be made for the helmsman's condition and the possibilities of relieving him. No one can remain alert hour after hour when wet and tired and cold.

If you do run before a rising sea too long and there seems a chance of broaching to if you round up, you can always take in sail first and slow down. Headsails come in easily with the wind aft, and if trimmed amidships the mainsail (which should have

link slides along its luff for offshore work) will also come down
—though a downhaul made fast halfway up the luff will help.
If necessary you can slow her down still more by towing a warp.
Soon you should have her moving slowly enough to round up
without risk of damage when a few smaller seas offer the chance.
Under really severe conditions patience at such a time pays off.
Skipper during World War II in the Offshore Patrol, John
Timken once ran before a winter gale for five hours, waiting
for and finally getting a chance to round up.

As a rule thunderstorms generate the strongest winds summer
sailors encounter. These storms raise little sea, but they can
blow so hard that reefing is not sufficient answer. At the same
time it's often hard to tell whether they'll blow hard or not.
Possibly I'm over-cautious, but when a nasty looking New England thunderstorm comes toward me I drop my mainsail and
continue under staysail only until the storm has tipped its
hand. My ship encourages this policy by her ability to go to
windward and come about, though not within eight points or
near it, under staysail only in a lump of sea. That kind of ability is a great help to anyone and suggests another experiment.
Next time it blows, drop your main and find out what your boat
will do under a small headsail. Knowing you can get to windward and maneuver under one small sail brings another dose
of the old elixir, confidence.

Occasionally in narrow waters, perhaps threading a channel
or entering a harbor, you have to run before a strong wind
without being able to put it safely on your quarter. Instead of
risking a jibe or worrying about it, try sheeting your boom
amidships and letting it jibe as often as it wants. You'll slow
down, but your jibes will cause no damage. With your rudder
you can forestall any tendency to round up.

"Slow down" seems to be my refrain. I think it's a good one.
I'd always want a fast ship, because she'll be more fun to sail

and, provided she is seaworthy, safer. She'll handle well under shortened sail, maneuver more easily, make less disturbance when running off before big seas, and she'll be able to stem a current and get to windward in a breeze. But when you're cruising, prudence must take precedence over speed.

The splendid record of safety set by ocean racers may sometimes mislead inexperienced sailors. This record testifies not only to the high quality of seamanship aboard most ocean racers but also to the potentialities of large crews. These provide plenty of strong backs to repair damage if it occurs, allow everyone to get his share of sleep, and let one man devote all his time to navigation and keeping the position up to date. A beginner may overlook all this and conclude that the charted ocean we sail nowadays retains few perils. He couldn't be more wrong.

I can quote no statistics, but as a random sample offer this: when my wife and I left the Bahamas, bound home in the spring of '61, we'd heard that three cruising auxiliaries which had started home before us that spring had come to grief. One had disappeared with all hands somewhere off the Carolinas. Another had radioed for help and been towed a hundred and fifty miles to port. The third, a schooner with two couples aboard, one of which had made the trip before in her, piled up on the beach near Hatteras.

Seasoned small boat sailors agree that a seaworthy small boat, well sailed, can weather nearly anything. But "well sailed" means with a lively awareness of the limitations of the ship and of her crew.

For a prime example of basic seamanship take Slocum, alone off the African coast in a strong wind and being overtaken by a pirate felucca which had crowded on all sail. The old bluenose watched the pirate gaining, felt the wind, studied the sky, and *shortened* sail—in time to see the pirate's mast go overside. Think that one over for sheer cold judgement.

The kind of judgement that got *Spray* happily and safely around the world enables ordinary mortals to cruise the coast with confidence and, experience gained, to stand out to sea for distant landfalls.

# CHAPTER XI

## *Windjamming*

Not long after separation from the Army in 1945 I moved from my native middle west and settled in Stonington, Connecticut. Within a year that salty town—the sea breeze blows through it, you see the gleam of water at the ends of its streets, at night you hear the harbor bell—gave me the cruising bug. Braving a huge ignorance of boats, engines, and the sea, I bought *Little Dipper*. She had an engine then, and I needed it to get me into and out of harbors.

But soon I discovered that actual sailing was not the half of owning an auxiliary. I had not only to learn how to sail her, as anticipated, but to equip and victual her, keep guests happy by putting them ashore on schedule, and on top of that learn to operate, repair, and prevent the explosion of what Coast Guard regulations coolly called a motorboat. I used my engine for two years, and then, taking arms against a sea of troubles, cut my troubles in half by pitching *Little Dipper*'s engine overside. That transaction still seems to me a classic example of logic and good sense.

Life afloat was vastly simplified. No more worry about fouling lobster pots. No more anxieties about cigarettes, drip pans, backfire baffles. No more work on spark plugs, coil, or stuffing box. A welcome reduction in yard bills. Guests forbore to make schedules, and so proved better company. When the engine went overside I began really to enjoy what I had bought a boat to get: the freedom and the zest of sail.

"Don't you get becalmed?" people ask.

Alongshore, where land and sea breezes alternate twice daily,

193

calms seldom last more than an hour or two. During my first six seasons of cruising the New England coast without an engine, cruising that included two trips to the not-very-windy western end of Long Island Sound, I kept a record of becalmings: *Little Dipper* spent just one night outside a harbor, which seems a good gauge of whether a coastwise cruiser is seriously becalmed or not. That one night occurred in Fisher's Island Sound. We anchored and all hands slept eight hours. If we'd wanted to, we could have been ashore for breakfast.

I often go sailing in the late afternoon. I have to stay a bit closer to home than if I still had an engine, but there've been few occasions when I missed supper. On all of them unaided sails got me home for a whole night's sleep.

People sailed and cruised long before engines, or the five day week, were invented. A breeze always comes. Since the world began one always has—along my part of the coast usually within an hour. It's hard not to feel that the widespread horror of being becalmed arises from over-conditioning to machines. When victims of this misfortune find they're not in rapid motion and not making much noise they fear that First Principles have been suspended and that something dreadful is about to happen. The breeze lightens, the sails flap once or twice, there is a moment of quiet, and on goes the engine. Then, *cough-cough-cough* and the good old smell of exhaust fumes—everything's all right.

Surely calm is as much a part of nature's program as breeze or wind, and calm can be enjoyed. Few things, it's true, so wear and chafe a skipper's nerves and the gear of his ship as a calm when the ocean is really tumbling. But in the sounds and coastal waters most of us mainly cruise the sea goes down with the wind, and a calm brings an hour or an evening of shining peace. When the breeze dies for a while at sundown, and land and sea pause in their usual busyness to stare in silence at the evening sky, as if reminded by the evening star of an infinitely vaster business going forward elsewhere, why shouldn't we follow suit?

Is the world's tininess and our own so bad a thing to be re-minded of? Suppose we're late for supper. Will Orion wobble?

Then there are those splendid morning calms along the coast of Maine, when your ship lies motionless at anchor and the air is thick o' fog, a fog in which you hear but cannot see the flight of gulls and the lap of waves along a nearby shore. Why spoil your chance to be a part of that magic quiet by turning on an engine?

People warned me that without an engine many harbors would prove impossible to enter. This notion also seems to arise from over-conditioning to machines. The only time I asked her to, *Little Dipper* tacked through the entrance to Port Jeff. She has twice been up the Three Mile River to Rowayton. She has never failed to pinch and carry her way in sou'west breezes through the narrow channel into Cuttyhunk's inner harbor. I can think of only three or four places between Stonington and Cutler, Maine, which a sailing vessel cannot enter except at cer-tain phases of the tide: Menemsha, Wood's Hole, maybe Quisset, York Harbor. Regulations prevent sailing through the Cape Cod Canal, but at either end you'll find lobstermen or out-boards willing to tow you for a modest sum. I don't think I'd care to challenge the Bay of Fundy's fogs and currents without an engine, but many skippers have. Pacific voyagers describe atolls which must be entered through breaks in reefs where cur-rent always races, yet Slocum did a fair amount of visiting around the Pacific in unwieldy *Spray*. *Little Dipper* has done some herself in the Bahamas, despite her six foot draft. Some harbors, of course, a windjammer enters late, by starlight on the evening breeze, but there's no horror in that. Pleasure, rather.

I remember an evening years ago off New Haven in Long Island Sound. A summer sou'wester had gone weak and died, leaving the Sound flat and silent under a yellow haze. The sun went down in a huge red halo, and for an hour or so the sails hung lifeless and the ship seemed held in a glassy vise. Then, aloft, the evening breeze began to stir. As darkness came the sheets slowly straightened to reviving sails, and the ship began sliding through smooth black water. That breeze never came down to the surface, but aloft it strengthened until my ship was heeling and making a good four knots. Stars came out, and *Little Dipper* furrowed through the dark mirror of the water in a silence broken only by the chuckle of her bow wave. Without roll or pitch, as if drawn forward by a magnet, she sailed steadily and quietly through the glamor of the summer night.

For a man with an engine that day would have ended with the dying of the day breeze, with the dissatisfaction which turning on an engine always brings. But that day remains one of the ones I think about in winter.

Then there was the September afternoon we got becalmed off the New Hampshire coast northward of Cape Ann. This was ocean, but the surface of the water went smooth, undulating to an easy swell. The swell might have rocked a steamer, but *Little Dipper* only rose and settled gently. The evening was clear, with fall in the air, and we put on jackets and warmed ourselves with whiskey. The sun went down, and along the coast lights brightened under a high afterglow of wintry green. Instead of eating in Rockport, we ate in the cockpit as the stars came out. And then, as in Long Island Sound, a land breeze breathed aloft and filled our sails. Strengthening at spreader height without disturbing the smooth glitter of the ocean's surface, that breeze gave us a beam reach for the lighted whistle off Cape Ann. The ship took an increasing heel and built up speed. Within half an hour, although the sea was only rippled, the ship was throwing out a roaring bow wave. She went charging across the slumbering ocean like a creature from another world. We raced past the light at hull speed, lee rail awash, and still the sea was only rippled. Once again the anchor bit into harbor mud nearer midnight than sundown, and once again a day that would have been a dull one with an auxiliary ended with a memorable sail.

It happens all the time. The breeze dies, auxiliaries turn on their engines, and within an hour or two I'm having a better sail than any of us have had all day.

"But how about the danger?" someone asks. "Shouldn't you have an engine to fall back on?"

I'm tempted to answer that when an engine has blown you forty feet in the air, there's little of it left for you to fall back on. Gasoline explosions happen all the time. In my home harbor I've seen the results of three. And actual explosions don't tell the whole story. Many skippers who have cruised extensively in auxiliaries carry vivid memories of times when such explosions came within an ace of happening on *their* boats. They sail for pleasure, but it seems to me they're shipmates with a solemn question: will the Almighty, who has saved them once, elect to save them next time?

Ventilators and warning devices help, but like other gadgets they can fail. The danger lies in the nature of things aboard a boat, in the fact that a boat carries her gas and engine in an enclosed hull from which fumes cannot drain out as they can and do from cars.

I'll grant that if a man's dismasted close to shore an engine may save his boat, but nine times out of ten an anchor will do the same. It's also true that if you're becalmed alongshore with a storm approaching, an engine may get you to shelter in time. But it seems to me that what an engine gives on such rare occasions it more than takes away when you're alone aboard your boat and have her going under power. (You should be wearing a lifebelt, but how many people do?) One misstep can put you overside. If it does, that impersonal engine will take your boat right down the horizon until the last you see of her is her disappearing masthead. You needn't be alone. Your crew may be in the cabin. Crews often are. With the engine running they won't hear your yells and will notice nothing amiss.

If you fall out of a windjammer, she'll round up into the wind and back and fill, informing anyone aboard that something's wrong.

For me, this whole question of safety has been settled by a hard-boiled reckoner of statistics, my insurance company. When I got rid of my engine, my insurance company lowered my premiums. They didn't ask any questions about my ability or experience. To charge a lower premium they just wanted the engine and its gasoline removed.

It often seems to me that in sport, at least, our age has reached a point of diminishing returns in mechanical progress. At sea, of course, no sport at all was possible until considerable progress had been made. Magellan set off round the world with two full crews, expecting half his men to die before he got back home. Still later, few were of a mind to contradict Dr. Johnson when he laid it down that no man would go to sea who could contrive to get himself into a jail. And yet, when progress has been given its due, it remains true that in any sport the brute fact of this or that achievement, that someone did get up the mountain or catch the fish or make the landfall, tells only half the story. The more interesting half tells how he did it, with the enjoyment of what experiences. What counts in sport is not achievement but its quality.

Today, thanks to progress, we can (though I for one seldom do) drive to windward in blows which only fifty years ago would have persuaded hardened shellbacks to heave to. Who nowadays gets embayed? Dacron sails have almost eliminated the chances of blowing out a sail just when we need it to weather an offshore reef. Radio direction finders have taken much of the difficulty out of fog. If to all this, it seems to me, you add an engine, you've dulled and to some extent denied yourself the very experience for which one goes to sea in the first place.

I'm far from questioning the value of all nautical progress (not me, with my dacron sails and a radio for weather reports and time ticks!) but only asking if, with progress as with such other good things as food and drink, there may not be a point of surfeit, a point where the price in money, bother, and complication may not turn out higher than the reward in pleasure. Different men will draw the line at different places. I draw it at the engine.

Listen to Commander E. G. Martin, British ocean racer and ocean voyager: "No one who does ordinary coastwise yachting and takes an interest in the working of other vessels can fail to see the change which has taken place in the last twenty years. Except in the racing fleet, it is seldom that one now sees what a fisherman or pilot would call a smart bit of seamanship . . . Seamanship, like other arts and crafts, is being destroyed by mechanism. I speak with feeling, for I myself have suffered from the disease, and it was only because I could not afford to install a motor in *Jolie Brise* when I first owned her that I discovered what was happening."

Martin goes on: "Meanwhile I found such renewed pleasure in handling the ship . . . that I lost all desire for a motor and realized that I should be spoiling the ship if I fitted one. It was only by degrees that I regained zest and confidence in handling the ship in tight corners—tight corners into which one ventured deliberately because under sail alone they could not be avoided, and for the joy of going all out for something difficult, believing that one will succeed . . . In many cases a motor is an absolute necessity, but if it is not, I believe a man is really happier without one."

I know I am.

I avoid much trouble and expense. I get those sails in the evening breeze. I think I come closer to my ship, to the coves and islands of the coast, the moods of the sea. When a windjammer drops his mooring to go cruising it's with a lift of heart and sharpening of senses which an engine and the certainty of making harbor at a scheduled time would greatly dull. The unpredictable comes in, and the unpredictable is an essential condition of adventure.

Unaided sail allows you to commit yourself to taking wind and weather as they come and driving such bargain with them as skill and ship can drive. For a weekend or a month you depend on that bargain for rest and sleep, distance covered, shores and harbors visited, and so for a weekend or a month you live a life that's truly different from the one you live ashore. You leave shore life behind, not take it with you, and a different tempo, a different mood and outlook refresh and recreate you. The realities of wind and sea, daylight and dark, resume their ancient power. The swelling of a thunderhead, the sifting in of a high overcast, a new slant to the wind, a rising sea—these become all-important. With them you live and drive your bargain, along the coast or far at sea, and they liberate you from that net of man-made things and social imperatives which, ironically, our dominance of nature is drawing ever tighter around us. Sometimes it seems that our drive to dominate nature endangers not only our freedom but our humanity.

Hear the Sherpa mountainer, Tenzing of Everest: "I have feeling for climbing to top and making worship close to Buddha God. Not same feeling like English Sahibs who say want 'conquer' mountain. I feel more making pilgrimage."

So do I.